Something inside her reached out for him

Staring up at the stars with the breeze lifting her thin nightdress away from her body, Renee relived the powerful moving moments she had known in Nick's arms. Overhead the tall palms were swaying and she felt strangely dizzy.

Too much had happened tonight. She had responded to Nick's lovemaking in a way she hadn't imagined possible, and it left her feeling weak and a little frightened. From the very first moment she had met Nick, she had known by instinct he would affect her life. And now he had.

Nick had taught her in the most exquisitely cruel way possible that she was indeed a woman, with all a woman's needs. But...was he aware that now only he could fill them?

The Butterfly and the Baron

by

MARGARET WAY

Harlequin Books

TORONTO · LONDON · NEW YORK · AMSTERDAM
SYDNEY · HAMBURG · PARIS · STOCKHOLM

Original hardcover edition published in 1979
by Mills & Boon Limited

ISBN 0-373-02346-4

Harlequin edition published July 1980

CHAPTER ONE

FROM the moment she stepped off the bus, she was stared at. Curious stares, not unfriendly. She supposed she was overdressed. Some even smiled into her eyes as if to reassure her. She was eye-catching, certainly, but —well, hopelessly out of place. This wasn't Sydney, or London or Paris. This was Garbutt, a cattle and timber town in far North Queensland. The women wore cool cotton sundresses in a variety of vivid colours; the men, tanned and rugged, wore bush shirts and shorts.

Renee looked as expensive and glossy as a *Vogue* model on location, but she didn't have the air of a working girl. She was an obvious product of luxury, a slender, fragile blonde. No one looking at her would have believed she was in need of sympathy, yet she had been deprived all her life, a poor-little-rich-girl, showered with every material blessing as a substitute for loving attention.

Her father was Harvey Dalton, the wealthy financier; her mother, Alicia, one of his greatest assets, an heiress in her own right, a beauty with a perfect figure and a superb hostess. Renee had been pushed off to boarding school at the age of eight, and after university, she had been sent to relatives in Europe to acquire, in her mother's words, 'an enhancing polish'. Nothing further was required of her than to look beautiful, act impeccably and marry the man her parents had chosen. Simon Nichols, the son of her father's business partner.

5

In the heat, she shuddered, faced with her memories. All that Simon felt for her was a powerful physical attraction, the thought of picking her up and carrying her to bed. Then, after he had her and all the things that their arranged marriage would bring, he would move quickly up the ladder while she settled down to a life of utter emptiness. She could never marry Simon: she knew that with an absolute certainty. Just another possession to add to his collection.

The bus driver deposited her luggage beside her and smiled: 'Anything else I can do for you, miss?'

'No, thank you.' She sat down on a bench, returning his friendly smile. 'We're early, are we?'

'No, just on time. You're being met?'

'My aunt.' She felt better just saying it.

'Then I hope you have a very happy holiday.' The bus driver saluted and walked away briskly, still basking in her enchanting smile, though it had a little touch of sadness in it somehow.

Renee glanced down at her watch and away from the sea of faces. Everyone was so very brown, and the heat was having some mesmeric effect on her. She hoped Katie would soon arrive—Katie, her beautiful mother's curiously plain sister. But Katie was awfully nice, a lovely person really, warm and generous and funny with a great zest for living. Katherine Anne Ingram, one of the finest women painters in the country.

For the past year now Katie had been living and working in North Queensland, because she found the scenery so fascinating. North of Capricorn was very different from the rest of the continent, very lush and tropical, and Katie's last exhibition, held in Brisbane, the State capital, had brought its multiple beauties to life. Even Renee's father, a highly discerning collector, had bought a magical study of waterlilies on a dark green lagoon.

How angry her father would be with her now, Renee reflected. She was no more than a miserable coward unable to withstand the browbeating that had come her way. Her father had always made her nervous and her mother in her own way was just as formidable, determined her daughter should bow to their superior judgment. There were important things to be considered when one was working out a good marriage; the same background, the same friends, keeping one's fortune in the family. It would be a business arrangement, and somehow love would come after. Simon was attractive and highly ambitious. Together they could reach the pinnacles of success. What was life without money and a house full of beautiful things? Alicia bought prolifically and her husband made no attempt to stop her. Her beautiful clothes, her jewellery, the lavish way she entertained, only reflected glory on him. Renee cared nothing for her parents' world. To her it was no more than a gilded cage.

The minutes ticked by and still Katie didn't come. Renee's heavy lashes fluttered and she glanced towards the phone booths by the wall. Perhaps she should ring? Hesitantly she ran her hand over her shining hair, secured in a thick coil at her nape.

It was late afternoon, but it was still very hot. A glorious poinciana shaded the entrance and as she gazed that way she saw the bus driver point her out to a tall, lean man dressed exactly like a character in a Western movie; a red bandana knotted carelessly around a brown throat, a faded blue denim shirt and close fitting jeans, dust speckled high riding boots, a cream stetson with a fancy snakeskin band slouched at both sides and set at a rakish angle on crisp jet black curls. He turned his head swiftly and even at that distance she caught the silver glitter of his eyes—strange eyes, almost transparent against darkly tanned skin. Whatever were they saying?

She didn't have to wait long to find out, for the tall man made directly for her with all the sleek, co-ordinated grace of a black panther, his gaze catching hers.

'Lady, you look lost!'

His voice was very attractive, faintly derisive, and she looked so startled it further twisted the smile on his mouth. 'Well, aren't you?'

There was something about him she seemed to recognise—the lancing glance, the look of power, the hard masculine authority that weighed her up and found her wanting. He reminded her of her father. A hard, cool, self-contained man.

'I'm being m-met,' she stammered faintly.

'Are you sure?' His voice was dry.

'Yes, thank you. Thank you.' She said it again, hoping he would go away. Men like him disturbed her. Despite his fancy dress she knew he wasn't any ordinary cowboy. He was far too self-assured, too smooth and polished.

His black brows drew together abruptly in a frown. 'You couldn't be Renee, could you?'

'I don't understand.' She wondered how he could possibly know.

'Then you are!' he said crisply, his eyes on her hair

and her face and her lovely expensive clothes. Even her legs weren't missed—long and slender, the heels of her shoes ridiculously fine and high.

'How did you know?' Her green eyes looked harassed.

'Katie has a photo of you on her piano,' he explained tersely. 'You were only about ten at the time, but you haven't changed much. Still that little girl lost look. Allow me to introduce myself. I'm Nick Garbutt, your aunt's nearest neighbour. There's no need to look so panic-stricken.'

'I'm not!' It was incredible, but she was shaking and she couldn't hide it. Not from those eyes.

'You're not on the run, are you?' he asked bluntly. 'Katie's told me many times about her beautiful niece. What brings her here?'

'I want to see Katie.'

'Then you must be in some kind of trouble.' He was looking at her closely, noting the small pulse that hammered away in her throat. 'Does she know you're coming?'

'Yes, of course!' The faintest tinge of anger coloured her soft, gentle voice. 'I'm waiting for her to arrive.'

He gave her a masked smile. 'Then we'd better check it out. Either you've mixed up your dates, or Katie's working and forgotten the time.'

Renee didn't answer this, though it had already crossed her mind. She hated that mocking look in his eyes, the disconcerting glint of irony. 'I'd better ring,' she said, and made as if to move.

'Allow me!' He bowed rather suavely. 'I think perhaps you're under some emotional stress.'

'No.' Her beautiful eyes lifted.

'Well, never mind!' He gave a faint shrug of those wide shoulders. 'I'll go and ring Katie. While I'm there I'll congratulate her on her beautiful niece. Far too beautiful, if you don't mind my saying so.'

Flustered and on edge, she watched him walk away to the phone booths. If he had already weighed her up as a lightweight she had drawn her conclusions about him. She had never met such an outspoken man in her whole life. He was striking she supposed; a good head, straight nose, high cheekbones and a well formed mouth, but his cleft chin was aggressive and she couldn't imagine him inhabiting her world at all. He looked hard and tough and the sparkling eyes turned her way were full of dancing mocking lights. She wondered if he was married. Pity the woman—he looked like a law unto himself.

It seemed ages before anyone answered, then she saw his mouth moving and caught the white flash of his smile. He had excellent teeth and the hand holding the phone to his ear was long-boned and rather clever-looking. Beside him, slim, elegant Simon would look like a puppet. They would both be around the same age, the early thirties, but this man was already where he wanted to be. Belatedly she remembered his sur-name was the same as the town. When she had last seen Katie at her Brisbane exhibition she had never men-tioned anyone of that name, yet he appeared to know Katie well.

He was coming back to her, lifting a casual hand as he was greeted constantly. Apparently he was very well known and she caught the gleam in more than one woman's eye which made her wonder again if he were married.

'Well?' Her voice sounded cool and brittle even to herself, when really he was making her shake with nerves.

'Katie had you arriving on Friday. Now I've plunged her into shock.'

'But ...' Renee's white-clad shoulders lifted a little desperately, 'I did say the twenty-first.'

'You stammer a little when you're nervous. Actually it's rather charming. Katie thought you said the twenty-third, but no matter. She sends her love and abject apologies and I'm to take you to her now.' Very masterfully he took charge of her expensive luggage. 'The car is parked not far from here. I'm sure you'll like it a whole lot better than the bus station. For one thing it's air-conditioned, and that camellia skin has changed colour.'

She had no recourse other than to go with him. She was above average height herself, but he made her feel tiny, glancing down at her sideways out of those silver, mocking eyes. 'Don't rush,' he said smoothly. 'You don't care for the heat?'

'I think I'll enjoy it,' she returned evenly. 'It's so warm and soft it's having a peculiarly soporific effect at the moment.'

'You've had a long day.'

She nodded and looked away. 'I've just realised your surname is the same as the town.'

'We have a small stake in it.' He gave her a sharp smile.

'You have a property, perhaps?' She looked up at him briefly, her eyes touching the cream Stetson and the collar of his carelessly buttoned denim shirt.

'I hope you'll visit it.' The hint of mockery was there

again under the pleasant invitation. 'Emerald Downs. It spreads right back into the hinterland. We run cattle and breed horses. Some of them I race.'

'Do you really?' Interest broke over her cool, faintly aloof face. 'The only racecourse I've ever been to is Flemington for the Melbourne Cup.'

'Where I'm sure you were photographed endlessly.' His glance swept her beautiful white two-piece outfit that positively breathed an exclusive label.

'I don't seek it, you know,' she said quietly.

'Lord, no—it's just that the cameramen fall flat on their faces.'

They passed a row of parked cars and he stopped at the rear of a big, late-model station wagon. 'Are you going to stay long? Katie is thrilled to have you, you know.'

'I know.' Renee made a little gesture with her hands. 'She's the nicest, kindest person in the world.'

'And you couldn't stay home.' He touched her elbow lightly and directed her into the passenger seat of the car.

His comment stunned her and for a minute she closed her eyes. He must know why she was here. Did Katie tell him, and why? It gave her a funny vulnerable feeling, so that when he finally joined her, she averted her profile.

'Did Katie tell you why I'm here?' she asked huskily.

'My dear child, she merely said you were in need of a ... holiday.'

She looked at him then, stung by his tone. 'Katie has been my favourite aunt since I was a child. She's helped me enormously at different times.'

'And you're in some particular difficulty?' His light

eyes were probing.

'I don't think I have to answer your questions,' she said in a low voice. 'I'm grateful to you for your help. . . .'

'But of course, you don't have to tell me anything.' He gave her another one of his sharp smiles. 'I'm quite smart enough to figure it out. You're unhappy about some man.'

'Oh, really!' She gave a despairing little exclamation.

'Don't worry,' he laughed without humour, 'you'll forget him in a month.'

Expertly he reversed out of the rather difficult parking spot, ignoring her until they were almost clear of the town. Though Renee had little vanity, she was not insensible to the fact men found her beautiful and desirable, whereas now she had met the disconcerting exception. She had been polite enough to him, yet there was a hurtful contempt in his shining grey eyes. Evidently Katie had told him something of the family background, so he knew she had never had to struggle for anything in her life; except a warm, loving relationship, but he wouldn't be interested in that. He was a hard man with a challenging style and he had recognised her already as someone who would collapse under pressure.

The air-conditioning was so efficient she was isolated from the drowsy heat, yet when Nick Garbutt spoke to her suddenly she lifted green bemused eyes. 'I'm sorry. . . .'

'What were you thinking about so earnestly?'

'You, as a matter of fact. I was thinking you've taken an instant dislike to me.'

'Don't take it so seriously!'

'Then you don't deny it?' She smiled at him and watched his eyes drop to her mouth.

'Isn't it too bad you can't enthrall me.'

'I wasn't trying to,' she said truthfully, but he glanced back at her unbelievingly.

'Then don't precipitate anything by smiling. Even my granite heart goes pit-a-pat occasionally.'

'You're not married, Mr Garbutt?' she asked with gentle mockery of her own.

'Bright girl!' There were sparkles of bitter laughter in his brilliant eyes. 'I find it strange you're not married yourself, nor engaged.'

'From choice,' she said, and her lovely skin flushed.

'Tell me about it,' his eyes raked her profile, as pure as a child's. 'For such a beautiful girl you seem to be full of complexes and inhibitions. It's unexpected in a social butterfly.'

'And you're sure I'm one?'

'A sad little butterfly, maybe!' His expression seemed to soften. 'I'm sure you're an only child.'

'Katie told you.'

'Don't mind so much!' He raised one winged eyebrow. 'Katie told me lots of things. You know how she is.'

'And you couldn't escape?'

'I didn't want to.' He was openly mocking her. 'After all, in your own way, you're fascinating.'

'And you're a very rude man!'

'Make that head of your list.' He flashed a brilliant glance at her. 'It must be a shock to find you can't manage every man in sight.'

'To be perfectly honest, I don't like men at all.'

'Why?' he demanded as though he had tricked her into admitting it.

'I don't like their automatic presumption of superiority.'

'But we *are* superior, little one,' he smiled at her. 'Now and again.'

'Just as I said, you won't even take me seriously!' She turned her head to look out at the flying miles.

'Well, I've a feeling, *Renee*—may I? if I did, it might be the end of me.'

She didn't answer but looked out at the trees. The poincianas were blooming, a magnificent flaming scarlet setting fire to the landscape. They were only just out of the town, yet already they were encompassed by bush and vast distances. It looked very lush and unfamiliar, the earth flowering prolifically.

'How far are we going?' she tried to speak lightly.

'Just a few miles to Katie's.'

'It's very isolated.'

'She likes it that way, but we all keep an eye on her.'

'And Emerald Downs?'

'It begins at the river.'

'It's very beautiful,' she said after a moment. 'Beautiful and strange and untamed.'

'If you want to know more about this part of the world, from the earliest pioneering days, I have a large library at your disposal,' he offered in a smooth, impersonal tone. 'A lot of the historical records were written up by members of my own family and we treasure my great-grandmother's diaries. The North was once a very wild place and a man had to be brave and determined to conquer the jungle. There are lots of stories that might interest you. Stories about pearls and gold and gem stones; sugar and cattle; the sandalwood getters and the buffalo and crocodile hunters. There are even stories of the curses the black man put on his white masters. In the bad old days not so very long ago, the kanakas were just lifted from their islands and forced into labour on the cane fields. Life was savage with violent tempers and outlaws on the run. In certain areas it was the wild man's pleasure to feed his enemies to the crocodiles. We have our own resident debil-debil on Emerald, a myall who was speared to death by his own people for his loyalty to my grandfather. The aborigines were wild in those days and notorious cattle spearers. The cattle kings were the bad-fella white men and the stock were fair game.'

'And your family?' she prompted. 'I know nothing about you.'

'My father is gone,' he answered tersely. 'He was a remarkable horseman, yet he got careless with a rogue. My two sisters Anne and Louise are married. One of them lives in the bluegrass country of Kentucky and the other in Adelaide. My mother divides her time between all of us. I usually see her in the winter months when the weather is perfect. She finds the heat trying these days.'

'So you manage your property alone?'

Nick glanced at her with a half smile, then back at the road. 'To tell the truth, ma'am, I have a large staff. But let's forget it for a while, tell me about you.'

'There's not much to tell,' she said quickly. 'Sometimes I think I don't really exist.'

'Good God!' he exclaimed dryly. 'And you're prepared to accept that situation?'

'No.' She turned her head and the pure modelling

of her facial bones was very evident. 'You're quite right, I am in a state of minor crisis.'

'About this man.'

'I didn't say so.' She bent her blonde head.

'Come now,' he made a little jeering sound, 'what else could it be? Obviously it's not money, so it has to be love.'

'So go ahead, laugh!'

'Oh, I don't suppose I want to torture a butterfly.' His glance sparkled over her. 'Of course he didn't let you go, you ran away.'

'You make me sound a fool and a weak one.'

'Not at all. I'm trying to find out what makes you tick.'

'May I ask why?' she said a little bitterly.

'Katie is my friend. I like her enormously. It's natural enough I'd take an interest in her niece. I've already heard a prodigious amount about you. How sweet and modest you are for a start.'

'You mean you think Katie gave me a lot of false credit?' Unconsciously she was twisting her hands as she spoke.

'No,' he said shortly. 'You *are* sweet, but so timid it hurts. How did you get that way?'

'It doesn't matter,' she said in a voice without emotion. 'Katie may be one of your favourites, but you don't have to like me.'

'No, I don't. Why the devil don't you assert yourself and tell me to go to hell?'

'I'm not much interested in you either.'

'Good girl!' To her surprise he gave a shout of laughter. 'There is a little steel in you somewhere. That's good.'

Now Renee was ashamed because she had spoken so tartly, but he was genuinely amused, his mouth wry, his silver eyes dancing. For an instant she had an irresistible urge to hit him, a gesture so foreign to her nature she was aghast.

'Thought better of it?' he asked tauntingly.

'What?' The idea that he could read her mind was unbearable.

'You wanted to hit me. Your eyes turned to jade.'

'I hate men like you,' she said in a shaken little voice. 'I've known them for years.'

'Really?' His dark face tautened and her fright increased. 'That's an outrageous statement. You've never known a man in your life.'

'I know men who like power.'

'Let's start at the beginning. Tell me about your parents. Your father.'

'Where's Katie?' she wailed.

'All right, stop worrying.' He gave her such a strange look. 'Maybe this ... holiday is just what you want. You're a very unusual girl and it's going to take time to find out your hidden secrets.'

'I'm definitely not going to discuss them with you.'

'You betray yourself every time you open your mouth. One thing's certain, you're frightened of men.'

'You're mad! I have many friends in my circle.'

'You didn't *know* it?' He glanced at her with a mixture of pity and contempt. 'Don't cry.'

'You're cruel,' she muttered.

'But realistic. You dislike learning about yourself. It takes guts to break out of a prison.' As he spoke he swung off the road on to a dirt track. 'Katie is renting the farm ahead. As you see, it's quite isolated, but she's under my protection. The land belongs to me and no one will bother you. For all our sakes, try to get that wounded expression off your face.'

'Certainly.' Renee turned down the sun visor, looked in the mirror at the back of it, then put it away. In the softening light her eyes were huge and very green, her soft, full mouth more vulnerable than usual. What an impossible man! What he wanted he had and if he wanted more he took that as well. She had grown up in a despotic family, yet she had never met anyone so brutal.

The sunset was turning the sky to a glory. She had never seen anything like it, the crimson, rose pink, the gold and the amethyst, mixed together brilliantly. They were approaching the farmhouse now, a white high-set bungalow with green shutters and a rust red iron roof. Everywhere the eye looked there were trees in flower, the glorious poincianas and the jacarandas, the dazzling yellow of cascara and cassias, the frangipani and oleanders that seemed to grow wild.

'I've never seen so many exotic trees!' Renee cried with a quick appreciation of beauty. 'It's really what makes the North so distinctive, isn't it, all this prolific flowering?'

'It's always like this on the verge of the Wet. All the trees and the plants seem to know the rain's coming,' Nick commented indulgently.

They drove through the entrance, a magnificent ramshackle archway of dusky pink bougainvillea and on to a free-standing double car port burdened down with the same hectic blossom. It was beautiful, like a painting, the dark green of the landscape patterned with so many colours. Even the old wooden house enchanted her, the silver tank stands clothed in honey-suckle. Even as she looked towards the front door, Katie ran out, both arms flung wide with open-hearted love, almost tripping in her haste over the honey-coloured labrador that was pacing her down the stairs.

'*Renee!*'

Eagerly Renee threw open the car door, longing for that warm, healing welcome. Like a happy child she flew forward, folding her arms around Katie's much shorter figure, both of them nearly crying in their pleasure and excitement. 'Oh, Katie!'

'How lovely to see you, dear!' Katie hugged her niece tightly. 'Will you ever forgive me for mixing up the dates?'

'*I* will!' Nick Garbutt stood leaning against the car, smiling at them. 'It gave me the chance to run Renee out to the farm.'

'Nick darling!' Katie, in a colourful tunic, craned her brown-helmeted head around, 'I certainly am glad you're my friend. Thanks a million for everything. You'll come in, won't you, for a drink?'

'Another time, Katie,' he returned pleasantly, and bent over to pat the frantically tail wagging labrador. 'I'm sure you girls have got lots to talk about.'

'Oh, we have!' Katie looked back at her niece, her blue eyes, her best feature, glowing with pleasure. 'This is so wonderful, I can scarcely believe it. Renee leads such a crowded life I thought she'd never be able to get away to visit me.'

'She told me how much she wanted to come,' Nick Garbutt gave Renee a look of mock friendliness, 'and she's every bit as lovely as you told me.'

'Yes, *beautiful*!' Katie breathed, her artist's eye on

Renee's pale hair and fine skin, the lovely slender figure dressed in white silk. 'As soon as you can, Nick, you must have dinner with us.'

'I was thinking perhaps you might like to give a party to welcome Renee to the district,' he said suavely. 'I'd be delighted to provide the background. The house is big enough to accommodate a large crowd and they can spill over into the grounds.'

'Why, Nick, how very kind!'

Katie was looking at him with so much open admiration and gratitude that Renee had the enormous task of reassembling her own expression.

'Would you like that, dear?' Katie transferred her shining glance. 'Nick has such a lovely home!'

'Oh, yes!' she answered as though she couldn't see the glint of mockery in his glance.

'Are you sure?'

Even in front of Katie he was going to challenge her. 'If it's not too much bother.'

'I think it's beautiful, absolutely beautiful of you, Nick!' Katie commented. 'I insist you accept the painting on my easel now.'

'I'll buy it, Katie,' he answered. 'A first class investment. How is it coming anyway?'

'Well!' Katie said happily, then reached across to grab the labrador's collar. 'I'll have to hold Honey so she won't follow you.'

'I'll take the luggage up into the house first. It seems very little for a princess.'

'Don't take any notice of him, he's an awful tease!' Katie smiled. 'He even advises me about my pictures.'

'Extraordinary!' said Renee, with pink in her cheeks. Obviously she would have to learn to hide her own opinion of Nick Garbutt from Katie. Ordinarily Katie was an excellent judge of character, but she hadn't seen his worst side. Then again Katie was unquestionably strong, a brilliant, interesting woman who although she had inherited money still insisted on the right to work for a living. He would admire her for that. Katie didn't prompt feelings of pity and contempt.

She watched him take her two cases up the short flight of steps and deposit them on the verandah, then he came back to join them, commanding the eye with his height and his lean powerful physique. 'I see Honey's happy to welcome another member into the household,' he said lightly.

'Nick found her for me,' said Katie smilingly. 'She's a wonderful companion and an excellent watchdog.'

'You wouldn't think so now,' Nick murmured dryly. 'I can't think you had a pet as a child,' he added, watching Renee pat the labrador rather awkwardly.

'That wasn't her fault!' Katie's tender expression darkened. 'Some people don't care for pets or large families. I remember a sick and feverish little five-year-old crying for a kitten and being given an expensive doll with gold curls and a strawberry pink ball dress instead.'

'I've still got it,' Renee said with a faint shrug of her shoulders, 'but I don't remember weeping.'

'I do. I was there.' Katie patted her ruffled hair into place. A breeze had sprung up, shaking out all the scents of the garden so they flowed together heavy with fragrance.

'What do you think of Saturday?' Nick asked.

'Sounds wonderful!' Katie agreed benignly. 'You must let me pay for the catering.'

'I will not.' He cast her a brief smile. 'Get on to Martha in the morning. Tell her what you want. She's had all the experience in the world, and besides, she loves a party.'

'Who doesn't!' Katie snapped off a hibiscus and plunged it into her hair. 'Thanks, Nick, you're always coming to my rescue and I'm going to find some way to repay you.'

'Until Saturday, then.' He sounded crisp and cool. 'I'll go away and let you rejoice in your visitor. Glad to meet you, Renee.' His smile was very white, a little mocking.

'Allow me to add my own thanks. I never expected anyone would be kind enough to want to give me a party.'

'It's a pleasure!' His smile seemed to reach the depths of his brilliant eyes.

What a strange man he was, Renee couldn't help thinking. Intruding into her privacy, criticising her sharply, giving a party. Katie was waving him off happily and just at the last moment she raised her own hand. Not that it seemed necessary. He was simply being nice to Katie.

'Let's go inside,' Katie said with her heartwarming smile. 'You can tell me all about what's troubling you while I cook something tempting.'

CHAPTER TWO

'So that's it, the whole story!' It was two hours later and they were drinking their coffee in the cool of the verandah.

'Then I'm sure we'll be hearing from Alicia,' Katie said grimly. 'I'm glad you've come to me, darling. It was much the best thing you could do. No one can force you into a loveless marriage—it's inhuman!'

'Mother thinks I'll come to love Simon afterwards.'

'I daresay it does happen,' Katie said thoughtfully, 'but from the sounds of it you don't even *like* the young man.'

'I used to like him,' Renee replied in a low voice, 'but that was before I came to realise all he cares about —making a lot of money and being in the social swim. I'm just a prize to dangle before other people's eyes. There's no love, no tenderness, no real communication. I'd just be exchanging one golden cage for another.'

'Don't I know it!' Katie said severely. 'In a way you've been exploited since you were a child. You're not an aggressive person under any circumstances and quite frankly my own sister gets a bit too much for me at times. Surely there are plenty of other attractive young men in your circle? Why Simon?'

'Because Mother likes him and the Nichols are close friends. I've seen Father look hard at him once or twice as if he had some slight reservations, but he knows how to charm Mother. I think she sees in him the son she never had.'

'Go on!' Katie clicked her tongue disgustedly, 'your mother never wanted more than one child. I distinctly remember her saying, "One's enough!" when you were just a baby with a nursemaid. In that respect I think your father wanted a son, but Alicia went on so much he resigned himself to making money. Neither of them have ever appreciated their golden girl.'

'I've never wanted for anything,' Renee said gravely.

'But you had to run away from your own home.'

'Yes!' Renee folded her arms about her knees and stared out at the star-spangled sky. 'Would you call me a coward, Katie?'

'Darling,' Katie set her cup down, 'I'd call you a gentle, sensitive girl who's been brought up rather severely. Both Alicia and Harvey are very dominant personalities, but they haven't crushed you entirely. You broke away.'

'It's just that I think I should have stayed. I'm not a voluble talker like Mother, but I should have asserted myself. I'm sure your friend Nick Garbutt despises me.'

'Nick? Whatever are you talking about?'

Honey put her golden head on Renee's lap and she fell to stroking its ears. 'I think he must be a mind-reader. He seemed to recognise at once that I'd run away to you.'

'Nick's perceptions are sharper than most and he's used to dealing with people,' Katie pointed out indulgently. 'What did you think of him?'

'Very powerful!' Renee returned clearly.

'But then he uses his power lightly and wisely. He's been kindness itself to me.'

'I found him rather averse to social butterflies.

That's what he called me.'

'I told you he was a tease.' Katie merely smiled at her. 'Apart from your year with the Sevignys and you were closely chaperoned there, you've led a sheltered life in a very tight circle. It will do you good to meet all kinds of new people from all walks of life. Nick, I daresay, could buy and sell even your father, but he's dedicated to the land and to his people. The Garbutt interests are highly diversified and he keeps a lot of people in good jobs, not to speak of benefiting the State. The Garbutts have a colourful history in this part of the world and Nick is very highly regarded. I find him a remarkable man with a broad range of interests. He can play any part as well—the tough cattle baron and the sophisticated man of the world. When you get to know him better I'm sure you'll find him very stimulating company. He may shake you up a little, but you have a delicate strength of your own.'

'And how come this paragon isn't married?' Renee kept her voice light.

'Well, it's not for want of being chased,' Katie told her. 'I expect you'll meet Sharon Russell on Saturday night. Her father is the manager of Garbutt Land Development. She's a vivacious brunette and you'd have to be blind not to see how she feels about Nick. It could be there's a romance there. They see quite a bit of one another and Cy Russell is always up at the house—that's Sharon's father. Her mother died shortly before I came up here and there's a brother as well, a rather melancholy young man, but the girls seem to find him interesting. He has some position with the company, but I rather think he doesn't pull much weight. Cy and Sharon are the goers and she's definitely after Nick.'

'She must be very confident to take all that on!' Renee said wryly.

'Oh yes, Sharon's confident all right and I'm sure Nick could satisfy her beautifully. That's if he wants it, and he appears to have full control of the situation.'

'I can't see him giving anything away.' Renee drew back into the shadows, enjoying Katie's company and the velvet beauty of the night. 'Nothing of himself.'

'Who can tell?' Katie gave her rich chuckle. 'Just keep your eyes open on Saturday night.'

Renee laughed, sounding young and relaxed, and just at that moment the phone rang.

'I'll get it!' Katie struggled to her feet and Honey jumped up to join her. 'I've a horrible feeling in my bones it's your mother.'

'I didn't tell her I was coming, just that I needed a break away.'

'She'll know you're with me,' Katie muttered with certainty, and hurried back into the hallway. 'Just leave this to me.'

Renee stood up and followed her aunt into the house, her heart in her mouth. Katie looked like a belligerent little terrier and there she was hovering like a coward, frightened of life.

It was her mother. They found that out within seconds.

'Yes, Alicia, she's here!' said Katie, and smiled at her niece. 'You'll have to speak up, it's a poor line.' There was silence from Katie as the line crackled indignation and Renee closed her eyes.

'Why don't you allow her to make her own decision, dear?' Katie said into the mouthpiece. 'No, I don't think she lacks any such thing. You can't run your daughter as if you're running a business ... on the contrary, I genuinely love her....'

Renee could imagine the words rolling off her mother's tongue and still Katie continued to answer doggedly. Obviously she was being accused of being, if not the instigator, the willing accomplice.

'No, I don't want to speak to Harvey, dear. Oh, very well....' More reassuring smiles from Katie, then she spoke briskly into the phone. 'Good evening, Harvey. Very well, and you? No, I'm sorry, Harvey, I can't allow you to do that. For one thing I've already sent the child to bed and she's deeply distressed. No, I don't know the Nichols and I don't much like the sound of their son and heir. How *could* she, Harvey?' This very sharply. 'No, I don't find it in the least peculiar ... let me remind you I have a rather large income myself and it will all go to my niece. Wait a minute, Harvey....' Katie took a deep breath and listened. 'You're talking about your daughter, Harvey, and not an insubordinate employee. So ... yes, that's fine. She should feel a lot older in a month ... have you ever taken the trouble to find out?'

Katie's tanned, round face was flushed and Renee rushed forward to take the phone off her, but Katie waved her violently aside. 'No, Harvey, what you want is a mechanical doll! I know she's a wonderful hostess ... I know she's invaluable to you ... aren't we talking about Renee? Don't you want someone special for your daughter? No, I don't, but the thing is, Harvey, she doesn't love him. You were head over heels in love with Alicia, as I recall.... The truth is, Harvey, you don't know me at all. That's all right, no need to apologise, I'm quite happy being an old maid. I am, I believe, my own person, and Renee wants to be wanted for herself ... yes, she *has* always tried to please you ... that's very understanding of you, Harvey. Yes, I'm grateful. Does it matter whether Alicia never speaks to me again? Yes, there is a strong bond and she is unhappy. No, Harvey, it would be much better if you didn't come ... on the contrary, she belongs as much here as anywhere ... I'm afraid I have to go, Harvey, there's someone knocking at the front door. Yes, very well. I'll keep in touch.' Katie gave a dry laugh, said 'goodnight' and hung up.

'Boy, no wonder you took off!' Her straight brown hair was standing up around her ear and she fluffed it into place.

'Was it bad?' Renee asked earnestly.

'Your parents still hold to the view you're unfamiliar with your own mind.'

'They didn't take long to discover where I was,' Renee said.

'I believe your mother checked out a few other places.' Katie stood in the hallway radiating a quiet anger. 'There's something terrifying about Alicia these days. She likes to pull strings and make people dance. Actually I would pit her against anybody.'

'And Father?'

'He's not so absorbed in his work he hasn't noticed you're unhappy. He came close to being very rude to me too, but at least he agrees you're in need of a breathing space. Probably the only major victory he's ever had over your mother. He'll ring from time to time and he's made me promise to be ever vigilant, but you're free to enjoy yourself for a month. After that, I think they intend to talk sense to you again. You simply can't turn your back on the good life, and I'm to tell you, Simon sends his love and understanding.'

'I see. How nice!'

'Send off a little note in grateful acknowledgment.' Katie suggested dryly. 'I haven't lost my cool in years, but that sister of mine makes it easy.' She frowned slightly and readjusted a flower in a vase, a small, compact woman, attractively plain, with fine dark blue eyes and the glow of health in her tanned skin.

'Thanks, Katie!' Renee murmured, and kissed her. 'I don't know why I start to shake inside, but I do.'

'It's not a pleasant sensation the thought of being trapped. Twenty-two is no great age and you've been pushed to the limit. You need time to heal and grow strong. There's a sadness and tension in you that must have been apparent to Nick.'

In that moment Renee knew a feeling of tremendous respite. 'Oh, how good it feels to be here!' With unconscious fluid grace she whirled around her aunt, topping her by inches, very fair where Katie was nutbrown, sensitive and shy where Katie was positive and direct. Yet they had shared the same pleasures all her life. Renee found it easier to be with her aunt than anyone else in the world and now she was safe in her company for a whole month.

They talked until it was quite late and in the morning Renee awoke to the sound of the birds, chirruping and warbling and screeching so loudly she immediately got up and rushed to the window. Of course there were birds at her leafy garden home, but she had never heard anything like this melodious din. Quickly she slid the insect screen aside and looked up at the trees.

They were alive with birds and she gasped with pleasure. Brilliant, rainbow-coloured lorikeets, yellow-breasted sunbirds, and on top of the tank stand in magnificent splendour, a scarlet king parrot ruffling his green and purple wing feathers.

An unusual feeling of peace and tranquillity swept through her and she lifted her slender arms above her head and stretched luxuriously. Nature was so beautiful, so bountiful, and everyone was absolutely free to enjoy it. No wonder Katie wanted to paint this dazzling world. It was almost overpoweringly beautiful—and so fragrant.

Great blossoming shade trees and the fruit-laden mango trees surrounded and sheltered the farmhouse from the high winds of the monsoonal season and tropical vines climbed rampantly over every support. It almost seemed like a problem in the jungle sense except it was so spectacularly lush. Some of the plants she already knew; the showy morning glories that were pulling over or supporting the old wooden fences, she couldn't decide which, the king jasmines from Thailand, the variety of trumpet vines: but many more she didn't know because she had never seen them grown, including a large shrub right under her window with fantastic hanging flowers. Even more bewildering was the variety of coloured leaves and bromeliads, and Katie had told her masses of orchids grew wild in the open garden, only she had missed the flowering of the cooler months. The beautiful dendrobium was the state flower and it too grew somewhere out there in the warm, flower and fruit-scented wilderness.

Slowly she withdrew her blonde head and readjusted the insect screen. She had slept so deeply and peacefully she was certain she was in another world. Turning around, she picked up her robe, drew a comb through her hair, then went out to find Katie. The farmhouse had been empty when Katie fastened on to it, now it was filled with sunshine and colour, the unpretentious, comfortable magic of Katie's artistic decorating. There was something everywhere to please the eye, an antique copper kettle filled with flowers, Katie's paintings covering the wall space, pottery and sculpture and an assortment of atmospheric bric-à-brac. Some of her parents' friends considered Katie a little eccentric, but if she was, Renee loved it.

Katie was in the rear of the house, a light-filled room she called her studio. It was just like Katie, no nonsense but spirited, inspired with colour.

'Morning, darling!' Katie called a greeting before Renee had moved into the open doorway.

'Hard at it already?' Renee moved across the quiet room, kissed her aunt on the cheek, then moved behind her to study Katie's latest effort. 'I like *that*!'

'So does Nick.' Katie squinted at her work. 'The River Track. I get a lot of my inspiration on Emerald.'

'It must be wonderful to be creative like you, Katie,' Renee offered softly.

'That's all very well, darling,' Katie laid down her brush determinedly and picked up a cloth, 'but there was a time I would have given anything to be as beautiful and sought after as your dear mother. No one ever took any notice of me however hopefully I might bid for a bit of attention. Alicia started off in the cradle with adulation, but I used to break my heart waiting for a pat on the head.'

'Poor old Katie!' Renee put her arms around her aunt and hugged her. '*I* think your looks are very pleasing. They would impress most people.'

'They didn't do me much good when I was your age. Not with a fabulous-looking sister around. In the end I had to learn a thing or two. It was Grandma Ingram who made me slave away with my painting. She suspected I might finish up an old maid.'

'And what's wrong with that?' Renee's green eyes went wide. 'Does it make a woman less important?'

'Well, darling, it does limit the usual experiences. For my age group anyway. These days anything goes, but I didn't much fancy being an unmarried mother, though I would have loved to have had children around me.'

'Oh, Katie,' Renee said uncertainly. She had never questioned Katie's status in life, thinking her dedicated to her painting; now it seemed Katie had resigned herself, in a sense, to being let down in life.

'Never mind, *you* make up for a lot of things,' Katie smiled. 'I've loved you from the moment I set eyes on you. You've inherited all your mother's looks with the novel touch of scarcely being aware of it. Alicia, even as a child, was super-confident and knowing, yet a big part of your charm is your shy reserve.'

'I don't suppose confidence comes easily to me,' Renee sighed. 'I've never felt I could really please Mother or Father, either, for that matter. I can't handle people the way they do. I can't even pick up the slick patter.

It's unthinkable to me to play useless games. Mother calls me fey, but I think she means pretty dopey.'

'Then she must have forgotten how you graduated with honours,' Katie said dryly. 'Don't worry, darling, your mother has a knack for making most people feel unsure of themselves. Stand on your own two feet and look around. It ought to be fun to get out of your tight little world. Now, let's go and have breakfast. There's a beautiful pawpaw I picked first thing this morning.'

They talked while they breakfasted on the delicious chilled fruit, then bacon and eggs and tea and toast. Usually Renee couldn't manage a hearty breakfast, but she found herself eating hungrily, listening to Katie tell her breakfast was the most important meal of the day.

'Not in our house,' Renee spooned some beautiful golden honey on to her toast. 'Mother tends to only drink coffee until dinner time. She's fanatical about her figure and it really is beautiful.'

'Well, you're young and you need something more. You're a tall girl and there's nothing of you.'

Renee laughed, looking very young and relaxed. 'Tell me, where did you get all your lovely pottery?'

'You like it?' Katie seemed to go pink with gratification. 'This is all domestic ware, but I have some beautiful exhibition pieces. Probably you've heard of him. He's one of the finest craftsmen in the country, gone bush. Harry Caswell.'

'Of course, H.C.' Renee turned a bowl upside down and studied it. 'He's a sculptor as well, isn't he?'

'He's a remarkable man altogether. He was trained as a sculptor initially, then he developed an interest in clay as a medium. He can do anything with his hands

—fix a car or a piece of machinery, build a house, even paint. He's a great big dramatic man. You must meet him.'

'So where does he live?' Renee paused to look across at her aunt. Katie was holding a cup of tea unheeded, her blue eyes very soft and bright.

'Nick sold him a bit of land about five or six miles away. He's been very kind to the artists' colony. There's another young fellow around, Ken Thomas, struck on our northern light. He's been turning out a lot of highly colourful stuff; a mixture of flora and fauna and exotic native girls. I believe it sells.'

'So let's get back to Harry,' Renee gave a little snort of laughter. 'Do you find him attractive?'

'Now, now, don't go getting any ideas, my girl!' Katie set her cup down and reached for the teapot. 'Harry keeps well away from women, even harmless old maids like me. He was married years ago, but his wife died of cancer. He told me she suffered so dreadfully he used to pray for her release.'

'Poor man!' Renee sighed gustily. 'He must have a liking for you anyway, Katie. I noticed all these pots last night.'

'Oh yes,' Katie remarked absently, 'Harry likes me, I'm told, although we quarrel occasionally—mostly about our work. Both of us are quite content to end our days happily here in the North. If only he would listen to me about mounting a major exhibition. He's been doing some wonderful things lately—robust, sculptural stuff, full of form and tactility.'

'I'm looking forward to meeting him,' Renee exclaimed warmly. 'Especially as he can bring the colour to your cheeks. No matter what you say, Katie, you're a very attractive woman, the kind one takes to the heart.'

'Don't expect Harry to appreciate me like you do,' Katie said wryly, finishing the last drop of her tea with satisfaction. 'Now, before I take you on tour of the orchard I must ring Martha. She's been the Garbutt housekeeper for years, and a fine type of woman. I'll offer to give her a helping hand, but she won't want it. She's a superb cook and she loves parties. Nick entertains a lot and Martha's trained a good household staff.'

'How many are you thinking of inviting?' Renee knew a moment of nervous dread.

'About thirty or forty,' Katie waved a hand carelessly. 'Just a small party. Don't be nervous, darling. The people up here are very warm and friendly and they do love a get-together. Besides, I want to show you off.'

Renee accepted this meekly, but she didn't feel she was the sort of person to make much of an impression. It was her mother who was the goddess, high above her and far out of reach. Although as Katie said she had inherited her mother's blonde beauty, it was evident she had not inherited her ego or her powers. She was just a young woman who didn't really signify. She didn't even have Katie's talent.

While Katie went off to do the phoning, she cleared the table, then washed and wiped the dishes, putting them away in the cabinets that lined one wall. Open storage shelves above them displayed a wide range of Harry Caswell's pottery; tea and coffee pots, earthenware dishes, beautifully glazed bowls that could be used for anything, lidded jars and biscuit barrels.

There wasn't a piece that didn't give her pleasure and she held a beautiful little teapot in her hand with a peach bloom on copper red, enjoying the shape and the feel of it. For some reason it seemed important to her now to find some creative outlet, some basis for self-expression. She would have loved to have learnt how to cook, for instance—haute cuisine stuff. Cooking was an art, a craft, even a science, but her mother had vetoed the cooking classes. For all her brilliance as a hostess, Alicia's activities started outside the kitchen door. They had a highly professional chef, who for the most part kept everyone out of his kitchen, so there never had been the opportunity to learn anything. At least she seemed to know how to tidy up.

After a quick shower, she made up lightly, debating what to wear. In her mad flight she hadn't been clever with her selection. Nothing seemed simple or casual enough, even the resort clothes. In the end she pulled out a sleeveless georgette dress in a soft shade of cinnamon and put it on. It was cool and it was bare with the tiny covered buttons undone and perhaps later she could look around for some little sundresses in the town. She didn't want to look special at all, yet she couldn't seem to work it any other way.

The weather outside was brilliant but hot and she remembered now she hadn't brought a hat. Katie was still sitting on the carved wooden chest in the hallway talking, so she walked down the front stairs and out into the garden. It was a wonderfully picturesque old place, the scents from the garden hot and fragrant. There were fruit trees in abundance; banana, mango, pawpaw and guava. There were even coconut palms and a grove of glossy citrus trees. Once the property had been worked as a small dairy farm until the owner had died and his daughter, who had moved away to the city on her marriage, had sold out to Nick Garbutt.

With the thought of him came the sensation of prickling on her skin. In her mind's eyes she saw that dark face turned towards her. He had the lightest eyes she had ever seen. And the most alive. Or maybe that was the dark tan. He was an infinitely disturbing man. He had even invaded her sleep, giving her dream an unfamiliar flavour.

She reached up to a huge, ripening bunch of bananas and snapped off a lady finger. It was good, so good she thought she had never tasted a banana before. She would have to go back to the house to gather sunglasses, the light was so dazzling. She had almost reached the carport when she heard the unmistakable sound of a vehicle approaching. She stood there hesitating for a moment, then a yellow station wagon swept through the floral archway and came to an abrupt stop in the shade of the poinciana. A girl got out in a delicious red ruffled sundress and came towards Renee holding out her hand.

'Hello there! You must be Renee. I'm Sharon— Sharon Russell.'

'I've heard about you, Sharon.' Renee took the other girl's hand. Although she wasn't a girl exactly. On closer inspection Renee could see the maturity in her face. She was perhaps twenty-seven or twenty-eight, but with pert youthful features and a delectable very slightly plump petite figure. Only the dark eyes nonplussed her. They were very bright, but the expression in them was just a little ... hard? Examining

Renee from the tip of her shining blonde head right down to her sandalled feet.

'I just had to come and meet you,' Sharon explained vivaciously. 'Nick told me all about your plight yesterday, poor thing.'

'It was nothing,' Renee made herself laugh. 'Just a mix up with the dates. Won't you come inside? Katie's busy making phone calls.'

'Yes, I know.' Sharon made it sound as though there was precious little that went on she wasn't aware of. 'It's not the first time Nick's given a party for a visitor.'

'It's very kind of him.' Although she was smiling brilliantly Renee had the feeling Sharon didn't like her.

'Well, why not?' Sharon showed her excellent little teeth. 'Nick's nothing if not generous. I was just a little—surprised. Katie didn't mention your visit the last time I ran into her.'

'She only found out herself a short time ago. I wanted to surprise her.'

'You've surprised us all!' Sharon's dark eyes ranged critically over Renee's tall slender figure once more. 'You're not in the least like Katie, are you?'

'Unfortunately not.' Renee took an involuntary step forward as a magnificent butterfly swooped down from the dark green foliage to spread its iridescent blue wings in the sunlight. 'I say, isn't that gorgeous?'

'You'll see plenty of butterflies up here. Especially around the lantana,' Sharon told her. 'That one is fairly common, a Ulysses.'

'I've never seen a butterfly of that size before, let alone the brilliant colour. This is really a dazzling world.'

'How long are you planning on staying?' Sharon turned her face up to smile.

'I'm not sure!' Renee lifted her shoulders in a delicate shrug. 'I've more or less been promised a month.'

'By whom?' Sharon looked sharp and eager. 'With your looks I expect you've left some faithful admirer behind.'

'No one I consider important.'

'But you do have a particular friend, I'm sure.' Sharon's small red mouth smiled mockingly. 'That's a beautiful dress, very chic and expensive. I wouldn't wear it around the house myself.'

'Perhaps you can tell me if there are any good dress shops in the town.'

'Good enough, but not up to your standard,' Sharon returned rather flatly. 'I suppose you're going to knock our eyes out on Saturday night?'

'I've hardly thought about it as yet.' Renee turned to walk up the stairs and Sharon followed, waiting until they were in the cool of the veranda before adding the cool query:

'So what do you think of our little town?'

'I expect it's very prosperous.'

'It *is*!' Fleetingly Sharon peeped into the hallway, saw Katie and waved. 'Katie must be having a time of it ringing round. How many people are you planning on having?'

'Thirty, forty ...' Renee shrugged. 'Would you like to come into the house or sit here?'

'Here will do!' Sharon sank into a planter's chair ruffling her glossy dark curls slightly. 'I'd love a cold drink.'

'Certainly—lemon, lime?'

'Lime will do nicely.' She looked over her shoulder as Renee moved through the doorway.

Katie was finishing her conversation in low tones, then she put down the phone and went out to greet Sharon.

'Well, this is a surprise!'

Renee waited for no more, but it seemed to her sensitive ears that Katie had sounded more breezy than welcoming. In the kitchen she assembled glasses, poured fresh lime juice over cracked ice, then put a half a dozen hazelnut torte slices on to one of Harry Caswell's brush-decorated plates.

'Lovely!' Sharon smiled as Renee passed her to set the tray down on the glass-topped wicker table with four cushioned wicker chairs set round it invitingly. 'I guess you're very proud of your niece, Katie?'

'I am indeed!' Katie laughed suddenly. 'Would you like a piece of my hazelnut torte with that, Sharon?'

'Very well.' Sharon had been about to decline. 'I expect I'll put on another pound or so.'

'It's very becoming,' Renee said diplomatically.

Sharon nodded and colour came up warmly under her olive skin. 'Nick seems to find the rounded look charming.'

'A bit of an enigma, is Nick!' Katie settled herself comfortably into her planter's chair, smiling at Renee as she placed the frosted drink near her hand. 'Thank you, darling. Well, I believe we've got off to a good start. I've made about ten phone calls so far and everyone is delighted to come.'

'Of course Nick's is marvellous for a party,' Sharon piped up casually. 'Are you inviting your sculptor friend?'

'Oh yes,' Katie rested her vivid blue glance on Sharon's gracefully reclining figure. 'He mightn't attend, but he'll get the invitation all the same.'

'Something of a recluse, isn't he?'

'In actual fact he's a good mixer, but when he's working he's simply not interested in people.'

'He should find himself a rich wife,' Sharon said pleasantly. 'He can't be making much out of those pots.'

'Far better to let him do what he wants,' Katie returned evenly. 'Harry is famous enough and he's not interested in being wealthy.'

'How extraordinary! I thought there was a greedy streak in all of us.' Sharon smiled a little thinly. 'Are you sure I can't help in some way?'

'It's kind of you to offer,' Katie set her drink down on the long arm of her chair, 'but I think we should manage. I've spoken to Martha first thing. She won't have anyone interfering at all with the catering.'

'Well, she does have a retinue of help.' Sharon allowed her glass to be refilled. 'What about Ken Thomas, are you inviting him?'

'I ought to,' said Katie. 'Naturally you and Cy and Philip are high on the list.'

'I'm looking forward to it immensely!' Sharon's dark eyes flashed wide open. 'Do you know what you're wearing?'

'I gave up trying to look glamorous long ago,' Katie laughed. 'Renee can look through my things and decide.'

'And you, Renee?' Sharon threw out a small beautifully manicured hand. 'Please, you *must* tell me.'

'I don't really know,' Renee answered truthfully. 'I've

a few things that might be suitable for a party.'

'Very well, keep it a secret!' Sharon exclaimed gaily, 'but please, I beg of you don't let it be red. I've a stunning little number I've never worn before.'

'Then I promise you it won't be red,' Renee said obligingly. 'Katie tells me your father is head of Garbutt Land Development. Do you work for the company as well?'

'Good lord, no!' Sharon sounded sardonic. 'I keep house for Dad and Philip and I'm usually at Nick's beck and call. He's the most dynamic man I've ever met. Honestly, it's exhausting at times and I'm often the go-between. So what do *you* do?' she added quickly.

'Nothing anywhere near as useful as you!' Renee gave an audible sigh. 'I had a year abroad after I left university and my mother likes me to accompany her to all her functions. There just hasn't been time.'

'Too bad,' Sharon said, and consulted her watch. 'I'm on my way over to Nick's, so I can't stay too long. I was expecting a nut-brown maiden with blue eyes like Katie, not a tall blonde.'

'Didn't Nick tell you how lovely she was?' Katie asked dryly, 'or haven't you spoken to him yet?'

The colour glowed under Sharon's dark honey skin. 'He didn't give an opinion at all.'

'Ah!' Katie turned her head upon her guest and smiled. 'He said some extraordinarily nice things to us.'

Sharon lingered no longer. She came to her feet and smoothed the full skirt of her dress. 'If you're sure I can't help in any way with the arrangements?'

'Just come along and enjoy yourself.' Katie picked up her glass and put it down on the table.

'It was very nice of you to call in, Sharon.' Renee gave her slow, beautiful smile that was totally devoid of any kind of malice.

'I'm so glad I did!' Sharon narrowed her dark eyes. 'Naturally we'll be seeing more of each other. You and Katie must come over to us one night next week for dinner.'

'I'd like that.' Renee had to remember her manners when actually she found Sharon's company rather trying.

'Until Saturday, then!' Sharon drifted to the stairs, an attractive figure in her vibrantly coloured dress.

'I'll come with you to the car,' Renee offered swiftly, but Sharon almost seemed to spring away.

'Please, don't bother. I think you'd better finish ringing all your guests.'

'I agree,' Katie said briskly. 'I want this to be an occasion we'll all remember.'

CHAPTER THREE

IT was the Friday afternoon before Renee saw Nick Garbutt again. Katie had gone into the town to collect some art supplies that had been sent to her and without her the farmhouse seemed oddly still and quiet. Beautiful as it was, Renee wondered if she could stand the isolation like her aunt, but Katie had assured her she wasn't in the least nervous even when darkness plunged their whole world into an inky blackness, full of flapping wings as flying foxes raided the mango trees for the plump golden fruit.

There were quite a few stories attached to the old farmhouse and without Katie's cheerful presence, Renee found herself moving a little uneasily out into the garden. There was a hammock slung between two sweet gums and she eased herself into it, swinging gently. The blossom-laden trees cast cool green shadows right across the side of the house and coloured petals lay all over the grass like confetti. She was just a little tired after the morning's outing; a long drive through the magnificent countryside, then a swim in a crystal-clear crater lake, so it didn't take long before her eyelids closed softly.

It was a tremendous feeling of relief to be safe up here with Katie. No arguments, no endless discussions. Not that she argued; she usually remained silent. Mulish, her mother called it. All her life, her role had been to do exactly as she was told. She was grateful to her parents for many things, but she couldn't marry Simon just to keep their approval. Mother found him charming and very attractive, as though that said everything, but Mother didn't know how dreadful Renee had found Simon's one attempt to force her into passionate response. He had lost control that night and she was still haunted by her distaste for him and her violent rejection of his lovemaking. He had called her all sorts of names as she got out of his car, his good-looking face ugly when denied what he had set his heart on having.

Perhaps she was frigid, though that was the kindest thing he had said. She had even asked herself why she couldn't respond. Simon was considered a very good catch and she had found him attractive at one time. When he had rung in the morning, sure she would be ready to accept his apology, she had refused to come to the phone. This had sent her mother into a towering rage, as if it was a matter of world importance. Barbara Nichols was her best friend. All of them had such high hopes for her and Simon. What was wrong? The questions had started in almost insulting fashion, Alicia implying from the coldness of her gaze that there was indeed something wrong with her daughter.

Was she completely without emotion? An hysterical little virgin when confronted with the slightest show of passion? God knows she didn't make friends easily, could she really afford to let Simon Nichols go? He had been so patient, an ardent young man after all, not a monster. If she was excessively afraid of the physical side of marriage, she obviously needed counselling. So persuasive was her mother's tongue, so stern and cutting, Renee began to question herself with despair. Even when her father entered into the discussion, endeavouring to be understanding as an alternative approach, Renee had found it difficult to explain her complete change of heart about Simon. Perhaps she *was* 'stupidly, unbearably, innocent ... inhuman ...' Simon's words still rang in her ears. He had put no one else to fright, he had told her harshly, rather the reverse. This with a laugh. All Renee knew was that with his hungry mouth on hers, his hands on her face and her body, she felt damaged. She couldn't possibly marry anyone feeling that way. She had even tried to face the inevitable storm bravely, but in the end she had had to run away. She was a coward, and inside she was hurting enormously. It was almost as though her parents had taken Simon's side, instead of her own. Simon was the understanding adult, she was the tremulous child. Tears pricked under her closed lids and she turned her head and fell asleep. The world seemed to be full of people who wanted to attack her. Except Katie.

She opened her eyes again to the sensation of petals falling on to her cheek. Nick Garbutt was standing a little distance from her, studying her thoughtfully.

'Do you usually cry in your sleep?'

She moved so precipitately the hammock rocked to one side and she would have fallen out of it, only he scooped her up neatly and held her for a moment in his arms. 'No one is going to harm you, Renee. We want to make you happy.'

'And I'm g-grateful.'

'Don't stammer.' He set her down on her feet, carelessly brushing frangipani blossom out of her hair. 'Where's Katie?'

'She's gone into town to collect a parcel. I would have gone with her, only I was a little tired.'

'So you fell asleep and had a bad dream?' The brilliant light eyes were watching her face intently.

'I suppose I must have.' Selfconciously she brushed a hand across her eyes, green and poignant. 'I didn't expect to see you until the party.'

'There are a few things that need to be done around here.' He glanced around briefly. 'Tell Katie I'm sending a few men over in the morning. They won't disturb you, but they can clear back a lot of this vegetation.'

'Oh, no!' She gave an involuntary little cry. 'Please don't touch anything. It's all flowering so beautifully.'

'Don't worry,' he favoured her with a faint smile, 'we won't spoil your little paradise, just cut it back a little. You wouldn't want a snake in your bedroom, would you?'

'I never thought of snakes!' She looked up at him, startled. 'I haven't seen any.'

'I've seen two since I came through the front gate. Harmless, I'll admit, but they could give you a bad fright.'

'You must think everything frightens me.' She couldn't help colouring.

'You do rather put me in mind of a high strung filly. One false move and you're up and away.'

'Would you like to come into the house?' She made a polite little gesture with her hand. 'Katie should be back soon.'

'Ten minutes, no more.' He glanced down at his watch and again she noticed his hands. They were well shaped, lean and brown and strong. She wondered how they would feel on her face. He would never have to fight to overpower a woman. There was such authority in his touch, the easy way he had held her in his arms as though she weighed no more than a bundle of feathers. 'Are you coming?' He fixed his mocking gaze on her.

'Y-yes, of course. I don't think I'm properly awake.'

'Then I'll make you a cup of coffee.'

'I like the sound of that.' She moved gracefully beside him, her hair glittering in the sunlight, the green silk of her loose tunic teaming with the cotton slacks. 'We had a visit from your friend Sharon,' she said, endeavouring to make conversation.

'*My* friend Sharon?' he came back at her unexpectedly.

'Yes, she came to visit us.' It was extraordinary the way he flustered her, yet she would have put her trust in him if they had been marooned on a desert island instead of a lonely farmhouse somewhere in the tropics.

'What did she expect to find, I wonder?'

'She didn't think I was much like Katie.'

'Not at all,' he said gently, and moved back so she could precede him through the doorway. 'From where *do* you get your remarkable looks?'

'Isn't there anything anyone notices about me, except my looks?' There was the merest flash of anger in her long-lashed green eyes.

'Lots of things,' he corrected her coolly. 'You haven't been allowed to develop as you should.' He followed her through the house to the kitchen, apparently unconscious of her aggrieved glance on him. 'Normally Katie keeps the coffee here.' He went to a cupboard and examined its contents. 'What would you like, instant or the real thing?'

'The real thing. That is, do you?' He made the room seem so small she sat down at the table.

'You're used to being waited on, aren't you, Miss Dalton?'

'You did say you'd make it,' she appealed to him.

'And you're quick to let me. Of course I'll make it. Your nerves could do with a tonic.'

'I'll get the cake if you want some.' She sprang up, eager to please, only to bring herself within inches of Nick's tall, lean body. Today he wore a khaki bush shirt with denim jeans and around his waist, narrow in proportion to his wide shoulders, he had slung a wide leather belt with a fancy silver clasp. 'E-excuse me,' she said breathlessly.

'Always apologising, saying how sorry you are. What are you sorry *for*?' He put one hand on her shoulder and held her still.

Her thick, silky hair fell forward over his hand, but he didn't remove it, or his gaze. 'You give me the impression someone has frightened you badly. A man.'

'I don't want to think of it at all. It was nothing anyway. This is absurd!'

'There's no way on earth I'd hurt you,' he said curtly. 'Let's get that settled at once.'

'I *know*.' Her face was burning and her voice so low it was little more than a sigh. 'Maybe it's just something about me. I'm nervous of contact.'

'Then you must have one hell of a time. Looks like yours would melt a stone man.'

'I'm the one who can't melt.'

He greeted this with silence and when she looked up he didn't look disbelieving or pitying, but amused.

'You're young, Renee, very young. When the time comes you'll enjoy being made love to by the right man.'

'Thanks.' She tried to smile and moved past him to the pantry. 'Katie has made a fruit cake, will that do?'

'I'll agree to anything if you'll come back and join me.'

She could hear the smile in his voice. Picking up the cake tin, she moved back into the kitchen, painted sunshine yellow with a white trim and a feature wall papered with field flowers on a golden ground.

'There's nothing Katie can't do,' she said, still cradling the cake tin in her arms.

'Then while you're up here you'll have to get her to give you a few lessons.'

'I'm not very good at anything.'

He reached for the cake tin and took it off her. 'Who told you that?'

'I don't want any.' She watched him slice the cake deftly.

'You haven't answered my question.'

'I used to imagine doing lots of things.' She sat down again, moving the copper bowl of nasturtiums so he could set out the plates.

'Tell me.'

'Oh, you know, creative things. I'm so proud of Katie, but I can't paint. Then I wanted to learn how to cook, but Mother thought it downright peculiar. She doesn't cook herself.'

'So why didn't you go it alone?' He lifted the percolator and poured out the coffee, pausing to give her a long quizzical glance.

'I don't know.'

'How old are you?'

'Twenty-two, going on twenty-three thousand.'

'And how old is the man you've run away from?'

'I thought I told you I hadn't run away.' She tossed her long hair back from her flushed face.

'How can I help you if you insist on telling me all these unnecessary little lies?'

'You're an impossible man, Nick Garbutt. Simon is about your age.'

'And your family want you to marry him?' He sat down opposite her and pushed the sugar in her direction.

'I don't want to get married at all.'

'Why not?'

'Not ever.' She crumbled a bit of cake but didn't eat it.

'What exactly is it you're frightened of? The responsibility, the total commitment?'

'Claustrophobia. I couldn't bear to be trapped.'

'It sounds to me as if you're not in the least in love with this Simon. What does he do for a living?'

'He's a solicitor,' she said, and began sipping her coffee. 'His father is the senior partner in a big law firm. He handles all my father's affairs. Our families are supposed to be close.'

'So you allowed yourself to be drawn into an arranged marriage?' he asked dryly.

'At least I didn't accept the situation.'

'No, you ran away.'

'As you guessed,' she returned flatly.

'And what happened after that? I assume you left a note?'

'I think I've had enough of this inquisition,' she said huskily.

'*Tell* me,' he insisted.

Wondering why on earth she should, Renee did. 'Then Mother called. Katie answered.'

'You'd lost your voice?'

'I'm sorry, didn't I tell you I'm a coward?' She let her glance slide over his face before she averted it. Foolishly she wanted him to approve of her, but he thought her a fool.

'Finish your coffee,' he said. 'It's obvious too many people have been ganging up on you. Let me see now, I wonder how we can toughen you up a little.'

'Why the interest?' she queried.

'I'd be happy to arrange it. After all, Katie and I get on famously together.' He smiled at her and she felt a hot little blaze in her chest. 'Have you definitely decided you're not going to marry Simon?'

'I never want to see him again.'

'Is he coming up here?'

'My father has allowed me a month. After that, I'm to come to my senses. Simon has even sent the message he understands perfectly.'

'He sounds dependable.' Nick laughed gently, but his silver eyes were as cool as the lake. 'Tell me more. You're an only child.'

'*I'm* going to have a big family,' she assured him.

'I thought you said you were never going to get married?' He stopped in the middle of pouring a second cup of coffee for himself and stared at her, his brilliant eyes travelling over her like a shock of lightning.

'I can scarcely credit I said that.' She jerked her

head back a little distractedly.

'Well, let's hope all the little girls are as beautiful as you,' he said mockingly. 'You're all mixed up, aren't you, Renee?'

'Are you trying to psychoanalyse me?'

'I hardly have the time today, but if you're here for a month ...' He reached over suddenly and lightly encircled her wrist with his fingers. 'You see, you didn't flinch away.'

'Was I supposed to?' She was staring down at her narrow wrist with his long brown fingers locked around it.

'You don't say what you mean. How did this Simon manage to alarm you?'

'I may be a very unusual person, you know.'

'Oh, you *are*,' he said dryly, 'but you're not yet exactly a case. A good deal of your trouble is you've been mishandled.'

'Is there something else you'd like to ask?' The touch of his fingers on her skin was so spellbinding she felt rooted to the spot.

'Not for the moment, little girl, so don't be sarcastic. Tell me, do you ride?'

He had finally released her though the pulse in her wrist was still throbbing. 'Oh yes, I love horses. Father had me enrolled in a very good pony club when I was very small.'

'So we've uncovered at least one accomplishment.'

'Oh well, it's expected.' She smiled a little and her full, moulded mouth looked very soft and tender.

'Well then, that's settled,' he announced abruptly. 'I'll take you riding.'

'You're very kind.'

He started to stand up and for a moment she felt peculiar, almost giddy. She had never been so physically conscious of a man in her life. The thought hit her so suddenly it dazed her.

'Well, what's the conclusion?' he gave a low, amused laugh.

'You're a very compelling man.'

'And that scares you?' There was humour in his glance, even kindness, when she had labelled him too early as ruthless.

'I'll tell you when I know you better.' She stood up too, looking at him with a mixture of grave bewilderment and intense concentration.

'Do you know how to drive?'

'Of course!' she answered in her soft, clear voice.

'Then that's another accomplishment when you told me you had none. I'll lend you a car. Katie is running around in a battered wreck. The last time I tried to get in it, I nearly got brained.'

'You're too tall!' Renee was startled and a little amused at the image Nick's words conjured up. His eyes were beautiful. And his mouth. But that cleft chin was very aggressive. She wouldn't care to cross him over the slightest little thing, yet she knew somehow he wouldn't throw hurtful words at her. He was too much a man. Not a petulant boy.

'Coming?' he asked, like someone speaking to a girl in a trance.

'Yes, certainly. I'll give Katie your message.'

She moved towards him until they stood side by side and he glanced down at the blonde head that would have fitted neatly under his chin. 'You're the only tall girl I know who manages to look both delicate and small.'

'I suspect it's because I'm not wearing high heels.'

'It's not that.'

Something about his smile made her heart jump. She moved forward mechanically, forcing herself into action, when a voice called from the verandah:

'Hello there! Renee? Nick?'

It was Katie, and as she called their names, Nick took Renee's arm and propelled her into the hallway.

'Hi!'

Katie smiled at him in delight. 'I didn't expect to see you until tomorrow.'

'And I'll bet you've got a new dress.'

'I have, actually!' Katie's face was a study. 'Who's been talking?'

'Not me!' Renee said quickly.

'You can't move a foot in this town that I don't hear about it.' He came close to Katie and tilted up her chin. 'What are you trying to do, drive Harry crazy?'

'Oh, Nick!' For an instant Katie looked as soft and confused as a young girl. 'Harry doesn't see me as a woman but a fellow artist.'

'It's a kind of game. Everyone plays it at times,' he replied. 'By the way, I'm sending a few men over in the morning to clean up the grounds. There's too much vegetation near the house and the bougainvillea is going to pull the car port over.'

'I've been meaning to do something about that,' said Katie.

'I'm glad you didn't try. It's much too hard work for a woman.'

'Thank you, dear,' Katie said gratefully. 'I didn't much relish the idea of getting out my machete.'

Nick smiled and turned to look at Renee. 'Come on, see me off.'

'Yes, all right.' She started a little at his briskness. 'There's coffee, Katie, if you want some.'

'Lovely!' Katie beamed on both of them. 'I must get back to my job of finishing that painting for you.'

'I told you, Katie, I'm going to buy it.'

'Oh no, you're not!' She even stamped her foot. 'You do a lot for me, Nick, and you must let me repay you.'

'I guess I'm lucky, then,' he smiled across at her. 'See you tomorrow night.'

'Care for a drink before we go?' Katie stood in the open doorway of Renee's bedroom waving a bottle.

'What is it?'

'Champagne.' Katie came straight across the room not concealing the pleasure she felt in her niece's beautiful appearance.

'Better not!' Renee smiled ruefully. 'It might go straight to my head.'

'It has that effect on me, but beautifully.' Katie moved quickly to put down the bottle. 'I love your dress.'

'You don't think it's too . . .'

'Of course I don't,' Katie said briskly. 'Everyone will be wearing their very best and you can expect Sharon will take particular pains. No, that's perfect.'

'You look pretty good yourself.' Renee turned around to stare at her aunt.

'It goes with my mood. You don't think it's a bit

cute for a woman my age?'

'Not at all. You look an attractive, aware, very interesting woman.'

'You've always been good for my ego, darling.' Katie came to stand beside her niece and they both looked at themselves in the long swing mirror. Katie was looking unexpectedly chic in a long, gauzy sheer cotton she had found in the Young Fashion department because everything else she had looked at was 'stodgy'. In any event, it was very kind to her figure and the colour was absolutely beautiful, enhancing the deep blue of her eyes. The thick brown hair she wore short and straight Renee had set in heated rollers so it created a fuller, softer more flattering curve about her face. Even her make-up Renee had applied, so a different Kate studied herself with pleasure.

'Really, dear, what a difference you've made to me!' Katie breathed sincerely. 'All my life, though I can put anything on canvas I can't paint my face.'

Renee hugged her and smiled. 'Did it ever occur to you you might need a magnifying mirror, then treat your face with the same attention you treat your work?'

'Even then, you're something of an artist yourself. I mean, your brushwork is perfect.' Katie stepped nearer the mirror to peer at her gilded skin with its becoming trace of blusher. The way Renee had made her up she looked a good ten years younger. Either that or her glass of champagne was making her see everything through a rosy glow.

'Remember Nick's sending the car for us,' Renee mentioned.

'Yes, he's terribly gallant.'

'Possibly he thinks we won't get there in the Datsun.'

'I suppose I could buy another car,' Katie murmured. 'I mean, I'm richer than ever when my friends won't let me spend anything.' She turned away from her extraordinarily pleasing reflection and picked up the wine bottle. 'I'll just put the cork in this, and finish it off when we come home. Otherwise it will go flat.'

Ten minutes later they were being chauffeur-driven to Emerald homestead and Renee found herself being inundated by alternate waves of nervousness and excitement. Katie was a mixer by nature, a party-lover, although she could do without them, and a good talker. There had been very few parties Renee had attended out of duty that she had really enjoyed. Her mother was always there, watching her as though everything depended on Renee's making a big impression. No social function would have been complete without the Daltons and both her parents were superbly witty, seen to best advantage among their own kind.

This party promised to be different already. Their driver, 'call me Charlie', kept them laughing for most of the trip, a natural raconteur and dry as bones. Miss Russell, he informed them early, had been the first to arrive, in a red dress that made him stammer and drop his eyes. This didn't suggest a turtleneck, and Renee had already noted Sharon's penchant for showing a beautiful bosom. Her own dress glimmered in the dark, a classical silk crêpe-de-chine in summer white, the top sleeveless with a deep V, the skirt fluid over her hips and long slender limbs. With it she wore her favourite jewellery; a matching set of gold earrings, gold pendant and bracelet. Because it was so hot she had tried something different with her hair, arranging it to the top of her head so her features seemed even more refined and her green eyes larger than ever. She knew she looked good in a cool blonde way, but she wasn't one quarter as sexy as Sharon. Or so she thought.

When they arrived at Emerald homestead, she couldn't move for a full minute. It was much bigger than she had expected; a single-storied building of fine proportions, built a few feet off the ground as a deterrent to termites and so far as she could see completely surrounded by verandahs. The entrance portico was flanked by vine-wreathed double columns with a beautifully fretted timber gable and spire matching the fretwork on the timber balustrades and the brackets above the verandah post capitals.

Lights poured from the house so it resembled a ship at sea and like the farmhouse, but much more successfully restrained were the tropical trees and shrubs flanking the house on all sides, a wealth of colour by day and a romantic jungle at night.

'Beautiful, isn't it?' Katie breathed in her ear. 'The original homestead was almost completely demolished by a cyclone at the turn of the century, so they rebuilt on the grand scale. It's about the finest example you'll see of an early Queensland homestead. The verandahs are essential in this climate. Of course our menfolk brought the idea back from India. Those, as you can see, are about ten feet wide.'

'Right, ladies!' Charlie ambled around to hold out the door for them, and just as he spoke Nick came through the open doorway, across the verandah, then down the short flight of steps.

'Welcome to Emerald, Renee.' He took her hand

and dropped a kiss on Katie's cheek. 'I've never seen you look so dazzling.'

'All Renee's work! The sparrow turned into a blue-bird.'

'I like it!' He let his glance linger on her, then turned back to Renee, still holding her hand so she had to remain by his side. 'I'm certain you know you look beautiful too. As fragile as a lacy vine.'

She had the idiotic sensation that she was trembling all over. Or maybe she *was*, because his hand tightened for an instant as if to calm her.

'I don't know what time you told everyone to arrive, Katie, but they're nearly all here.'

'Great!' Katie looked up towards the house expectantly.

'Not Harry as yet,' Nick told her as they were nearing the portico.

Sharon's fragrance reached them before she did. She was standing in the hallway under the first of a pair of matching chandeliers, her red silk taffeta dress a burst of brilliant colour, her pert, sophisticated face radiant with a hostessy smile.

'Katie!' she called. 'Renee! Oh, lovely, you've arrived!'

They all moved towards her, the dark eyes expanding as she made a lightning assessment of Renee's hair and face and the simply beautiful white dress.

She doesn't like me, half of Renee's mind insisted, yet Sharon caught at her hand as if she had just been waiting for the moment of Renee's arrival for the good times to begin. 'You look lovely!' she said warmly, privately thinking Renee's dress was rather too simple.

'Thank you ...' Over Sharon's gleaming head Renee

met Nick's eyes and she recognised a mixture of admiration and mockery. 'I take it that's the red? It looks stunning.'

'I always think one needs to be brunette to look well in red,' Sharon agreed complacently, then she turned her head and laughed. 'Well, here they come at a rush to meet the guest of honour.'

Nick, however, took Renee's arm and gently steered her into the main drawing room where a good number of people were already assembled and from the look of it already enjoying themselves. Most of them as it happened seemed genuinely delighted to meet her and though she had to smile a great deal it didn't seem the extraordinary effort she had known in the past. Wherever Nick led her, she found herself following, responding to attention in what seemed an effortless fashion. It was difficult to remember all the names, but somehow she managed, her cool blonde beauty hiding her nervousness.

For the first hour, everything seemed to swirl around her—the music and the laughter, the kaleidoscope of colours in the women's filmy summer dresses, the way everyone was so friendly and called her immediately by her first name. The house was perfect for a party with the pedimented panelled doors of red cedar folded back so the reception rooms flowed into the spacious hallway and the guests could circulate without the slightest feeling of being hemmed in. Again, it was furnished with great style and Renee found herself admiring the impeccable taste that had created such a special environment. Grand as it was, it was still styled for comfort with a mixture of antique and contemporary furnishings and a unifying flow of colour.

It soon became obvious that Sharon considered herself Nick's hostess and Renee accepted that she handled the role beautifully, her attractive laugh floating through the house as she divided her time between the guests. The whole atmosphere was gay yet completely unfrenetic, so gradually Renee cast off her nervousness and began to relax.

Sharon's father was just as she expected, a highpowered business man, very much like Sharon to look at, but Philip, the brother, was a surprise. He was quiet, to the point of shyness, so that he made even Renee feel like a skilled conversationalist. Yet somehow she must have charmed him, for no matter what group drew her to the centre of their circle, Philip was always there on the outskirts, his hazel, gold-flecked eyes riveted on her like a moth to a flame. It would have been distracting, only there was something about him that aroused Renee's sympathy. Whereas Cy Russell and Sharon had a great sense of their own identity, Philip was hardly listened to without being exactly overlooked.

All the French doors had been opened on to the verandahs and guests were already beginning to take advantage of them as a dance floor. Someone caught at Renee's hand, and as she turned a little startled, she saw Philip smiling at her with his yellow-green eyes.

'Please dance with me, Renee?'

'I'd like to.' She didn't exactly mean that, but there was no polite way to decline.

'You must know you're the most beautiful girl I've ever seen.'

'You're being very gallant!' She tried to smile, but his eyes were serious.

'I'm not trying to be,' he led her straight across the room and out on to the verandah, 'it's the literal truth.'

'Well, thank you.' She was used to unconcealed admiration, but why was he staring at her?

Unlike his father and sister, Philip was fair and light-eyed and although his features were good, they made no particular impact. He wasn't that tall either, so as he held her he looked directly into her eyes.

'What do you think of the house?'

'It's wonderful.'

'Of course. Everyone loves a party on Emerald. We can't do without the Garbutts, which nowadays means Nick.'

'You work for him, don't you?' Renee was surprised at the sarcasm.

'Most of us here work for the Garbutt enterprises, but actually I work under my dad.'

'He's a very impressive man,' she told him.

'You don't mean that?'

'Don't I?' Renee gave a faint gasp. 'Don't you see your father that way?'

'I see him as an extension of Nick. That's all he's ever been, a company man. I mean, long ago he gave his life to the Garbutts.'

'He appears to enjoy it,' Renee pointed out a little dryly.

'Oh yes!' Philip gave a tight little smile. 'He's the head of Garbutt Land Development and I suppose it's made him rich.'

'Don't you like working for the company?' Renee asked.

'All I want to do, Renee, is simply sail away. It's my fantasy.' His disconcerting eyes rested on Renee's face with a curious intensity. 'One day I'll find the courage to simply pack up and go.'

They were moving past a French door and Renee saw Nick Garbutt standing a few feet away, tall and dark and so vivid he made Philip pale away, although he held her in his arms, his hand sliding across her back as though he wanted to know her very bones. Nick turned his head and just for an instant Renee looked into his eyes.

'Handsome devil, isn't he?' Philip said softly, yet it made her skin prickle uncomfortably.

'He's been very kind to my aunt,' Renee answered evasively.

'Oh yes, Katie,' Philip said in an easier voice. 'She's a nice person, isn't she? Mostly everyone thinks Katie's a dear, and I do so envy her her talent.'

'So do I.' Renee gave him a half smile, not knowing it lit her face with a subtle, unconscious seduction.

'But you're a girl with everything!' Philip almost brought his hand up to touch her hair.

'Good heavens, no. I haven't done anything, as yet.'

'You're not going to be married—at least, engaged?' Philip asked quickly, steering her into the glimmering shadows.

'Not yet, Philip.' Against her will she was almost driven into comforting him. It was absurd, but his expression was anxious.

'And what does *that* mean?' The urgent enquiry confirmed it.

'It means I have no intention of marrying anyone at the moment,' she said lightly, wondering if he would ask her next if she believed in love at first sight. Imperceptibly at first, his arms had tightened so that now she had to lean back to avoid a bodily contact she didn't want.

'I hope you'll allow me to show you around all our beauty spots?' he asked gently. 'I know a good place to swim.'

'I thought so, you have a very good tan,' Renee answered diplomatically. He did have a honey-coloured tan that went well with his fair hair and hazel eyes.

'Then you will?'

'Thank you for asking, Philip. I'll let you know.' It wasn't a strong acceptance, yet he smiled as if a date had already been arranged.

'Sharon was saying you and Katie are coming over for dinner next week?'

'Yes. Every one is being so nice to me.'

'Can you blame them!' For a moment his cheek hazed her hair. 'I've never seen a girl as beautiful and poised as you are.'

'Then I'll tell you a secret,' she shrugged delicately. 'It's only a front. Inside I suffer all the same anxieties and apprehensions as everyone else.'

'Will you come for a drive with me tomorrow?' He regarded her fixedly.

'I'm sorry, Philip. Nick's already arranged something!' It wasn't in the least true, but she said it in the heat of the moment.

'Then Sharon's going?'

'I don't really know.' Now why had she told such a stupid lie?

'Well, you must have guessed that Nick has been monopolising my sister's attentions for some time. She'll marry him for sure, and not just for his money. She's mad about him, and if you doubt it, just watch the way she looks at him.'

'And it annoys you?'

'I don't like to see a person so overwhelmed by anyone else. When we were kids my sister was sweet, now she's so much like Dad it staggers me. I can't count a single happy hour since my mother died.'

'Oh, Philip, I'm sorry!' Renee's tender heart smote her and she looked at him with such gentle compassion he instinctively hugged her closer.

'It's life, isn't it? My mother didn't seem to care that my mind wasn't filled with a lot of silly ambitions. Dad has worked tirelessly for the Garbutts, yet he found it easy to simply ignore my mother and me. Up until now I've been a big disappointment to him and I guess I always will be. Sharon is the one who doesn't lack drive. She'll make Nick a wonderful wife. Both of them are as hard as diamonds.'

'You trouble me, Philip,' Renee said, and meant it.

'I'm sorry.' It was his turn to apologise. 'I never talk to anyone, yet I seem to have revealed myself to quite an extent with you. Don't blame me, Renee. I haven't had a happy life.'

'No.' Renee had a clear insight into what he meant. A comfortable home and money didn't supply all the answers: she knew that for a certainty. 'Yet I'm sure you've got a lot to be thankful for, Philip?'

'Sure, my job's safe, even if everyone knows I'm not much good at it.'

'So you've committed yourself to a cage?'

'That's good, Rene!' He narrowed his eyes at her so they looked almost feline. 'I *am* in a cage. I want to get out, but I can't.'

Renee was aware the music had stopped, but still

Philip held her, unable to break away from her green glance.

'Hey there, you two!'

In a way it was a relief, Sharon breezing up to them, smiling delightedly as if it pleased her to see them so apparently engrossed in each other. 'What are you talking about that's so important?'

'I'm telling Renee the story of my life,' Philip returned a shade bitingly, causing his sister to flush.

'Don't talk like that, Pip,' she said quietly.

Renee said nothing, feeling embarrassed on Sharon's account more than her own.

'Let me find you a drink,' said Philip, and laid a hand on Renee's arm.

'Thank you.'

'It's all there to be drunk,' Sharon smiled.

'Don't go away!' Philip called, then faltered as Nick Garbutt strolled out on to the verandah. 'Oh, hi there, Nick.'

'How are you, Philip?'

'Trying to get some fun out of life.'

'Then you're at the right party.' Nick nodded his head and moved away, a striking figure in a silk shirt and narrow slacks with a gold medallion around his neck. For a cattleman he was a very elegant dresser and his tall, lean body was the perfect vehicle for clothes. He looked like a rich man and a man on the move, superbly fit and confident.

'I think Renee here is tying Philip in knots,' Sharon announced gaily.

'That's just part of a woman's training, isn't it?' The silver eyes flicked Renee's profile. 'I mean, you all learn it.'

'Do you mean to tell me I could tie *you* in knots?' Sharon grasped his arm.

'You sure try.'

'Willingly.' Sharon smiled deeply into his eyes. He was so much taller, she had to throw her glossy head back and in doing so revealed the pretty line of her throat and chin. 'It's a fine party we're having, isn't it?'

'We really should leave it up to the guest of honour to tell us that.' For the first time Nick looked at Renee fully.

'I'm overwhelmed with everything!' A spasm of panic seized her that he was annoyed with her about something.

'But you haven't really seen over the house. I was just awaiting the opportunity to show you.'

'Not now, Nick,' Sharon gave a little laugh. 'Pip's coming back with a drink for Renee.'

'Tell him I'm showing Renee over the house.'

'Of course.' Sharon smiled at Renee without enthusiasm. 'This is a house I absolutely love.'

As they walked away from her, Renee was conscious of the dark eyes boring into her back and she sighed.

'What's that for?' Nick asked abruptly.

She lifted her hand a little and let it drop. 'Oh, I was just thinking, I suppose.'

'About what?'

'It's not important, Nick.'

As they moved through the drawing room they were stopped continuously, but Nick waved them all aside, telling them smoothly he was showing Renee over the rest of the house. Katie, in high good spirits, was holding court in a far corner of the large room and she lifted a hand and waved. So far Harry Caswell hadn't arrived, but his absence wasn't causing anything terrible to happen to Katie. She was radiating pleasure so that it warmed everyone around her.

Everywhere Renee's eyes moved, there was beauty and they roamed the large house with Nick explaining how his great-grandfather for the most part had imported the magnificent pieces of antique furniture into the infant colony. Every room held different pieces that were a collector's dream and Renee was fascinated by the whole Garbutt saga of imposing a highly cultivated civilisation on a great section of what once had been jungle. It must have been a nightmare even trying to get the furniture in, a lot of it massive by today's standards.

Nick let her take her time, watching her move slowly and gracefully from room to room. The library she particularly liked, its tall walls completely lined with leather-bound books in rich colours, the gold stamped bindings gleaming in the light. The massive mahogany library desk with its applied garland motif, Nick told her, was a Chippendale, and she went to stand behind it, running her fingers lightly over the rich carving.

'What a beautiful piece—and so many books.'

'It's my favourite room in the whole house,' Nick said idly. 'All of my family have been great readers— I guess they've had to be, there was little entertainment in the early days. A lot of the books here are very valuable and I won't pretend it's an easy job keeping them in good condition. You're welcome to browse here any time you like.'

'I'd love to.' She tipped her head back to look up the brass-trimmed shelves. 'Is it catalogued?'

'It is, despite its size.' Nick picked up a family photograph from a small circular table placed between two big inviting armchairs and passed it to her. 'The Garbutt family, when we were all together.'

'Show me.' Renee took the photograph from him in its gilt frame and looked down at the family group. It was impossible not to identify Nick immediately, a handsome teenage boy sprawling with indolent grace on the grass, flanked by two very pretty dark-haired girls, one of them with an arm flung carelessly around his neck. His mother sat in a peacock chair just a little to the left of the group with a tall man with Nick's distinctive bone structure leaning over the top of the chair. All of them were smiling, and Renee smiled back involuntarily.

'You all look very content and happy. There's love in that photograph.'

'Don't sound as if you didn't get too damned much of it.'

'Did I sound like that?' She glanced up into his face, looking first at his eyes, then his mouth, studying it. The edges were raised, giving it a very clean definition. She almost wanted to put out her finger to trace its shape. How strange to find a man's mouth beautiful.

'Where have you gone to now?' he asked in a soft voice that made her shiver.

'Sorry. I'm sorry.'

'There you go again,' he took the photograph out of her hand and put it down on the desk behind her so they were facing each other with Renee's head uplifted as though she were listening to a voice inside her. 'Tell me about your childhood,' he invited.

'There's nothing to tell. Nothing.'

'Nothing that made you happy. Tell me. I've been wondering about you.'

'Why?'

'Who was your special friend when you were a little girl?'

'I've forgotten. I know I had friends, but I've forgotten.'

'Have you ever been in love?'

'*No!*' From the expression on her face he might have thought he had shocked her.

'Why not? Can't you handle it?'

'I can't handle a lot of things. You may have noticed.'

'Don't get angry with me, Renee.' He smiled suddenly so the level of fright, shock, fascination, dropped to a height she could handle.

'I'm not angry,' she shook her head a little trying to extricate herself from some treacherous quicksand. 'My life has been nothing like as colourful as yours. There's been no death, no danger, no love affairs, no ambition. It all adds up to nothing. I told you.'

'The truth is, you're frightened of doing anything. Frightened to feel. I suppose in a way, you haven't grown up.'

'You seem to know a great deal about me?' She glanced very briefly into those crystal eyes, trembling in spite of her efforts at self-control. 'I rather suspected you thought just that.' The blood had quickened under her camellia skin and she moved restlessly away from him, gazing down at the pattern in a magnificent Bessarabian rug.

'Where did you go to school?' he asked her, ignoring her slightly febrile movements.

She lifted her head and mentioned the name of her exclusive girls' school, and even then something moved painfully in her. She was a small girl again, unprepared for her banishment to boarding school, struggling with her tears though her mother spoke to her sharply. The other girls were all standing around chattering, but she was painfully shy and moreover sick with the feeling of being abandoned.

'Sometimes I dream I'm back there again,' she said, and gave a wry little laugh. 'I was a good student, but I couldn't wait for those years to pass. It was much better at university and I loved my year in Europe. It was unforgettable really, the visual experience, past and present all mived up together, the art and the architecture, the faces that belonged in Renaissance paintings, the palaces and the pageantry, the birth of civilisation....'

'But no erotic experiences.'

'What if I said yes?' She faced him swiftly.

'I wouldn't believe you. There's no passion in your eyes, Renee. They're very beautiful and when I've hurt you they glitter like emeralds, but they're the eyes of a child who wants to postpone maturity for as long as possible.'

'You think I should indulge in a love affair?' She lifted her chin, regarding him with a certain imperiousness.

'Not Philip Russell,' Nick answered in a faintly mocking voice. 'I know you have a very tender heart and Philip's probably convinced you he's in need of your pity, but I'd like you to be sensible and not listen. If he's already decided he's fallen in love at first sight, he'll get over it.'

'That's absurd!' Her eyelids widened.

'Then you can't read the signs?'

The silver flash of his eyes seemed to burn her, searing her white flesh. 'Please, Nick, can't we talk about something else?' she asked almost timidly.

'Of course.' An odd expression moved across his dark face. For a minute more he looked at her in a deep silence, then he closed the space that divided them and took her arm. 'No more problems for tonight. No more trying to get you to talk. I'll try that when we're completely alone.'

There was no impulse to pull free of him and run. No physical rejection of that lean brown hand on her arm, yet something was happening inside her that made her body ache with the strain. He was a hard, strong man and any involvement with him would lead to a turbulent and painful chaos. It wasn't in her the grand passion he was thinking about, yet the touch of his fingers on her bare skin were sending shocks of awareness up and down her arm. Up until now she had never experienced such glittering excitement. That was it—*excitement*, yet Simon had held her frantically, crushing her resistance, and all she could remember was the deep and dreadful distaste. Maybe there were no cold women at all, only unaroused ones?

When they returned to the main drawing room, they found Harry Caswell had joined them. He stood in the centre of the room, a big, heavy man with silver hair and a silver beard and penetrating light blue eyes. At first glance he looked rather fierce, like an eagle impossible to tame, but as the minutes of introduction passed quickly, Renee could see the honour and kindness in his eyes. His voice for such a big man was quiet, with an occasional deep burst of laughter, and Renee decided she liked him enormously. In some way she felt as comfortable with him as she did with Katie, so they slipped very easily into a companionable conversation that Sharon for one appeared to resent. When Nick was watching over his guest of honour and not making the slightest effort to break away from Harry Caswell and Katie and the rest of them, it was obvious he was neglecting her. Nor did she care for Harry Caswell, the confidence in the man when he wore such dreadful clothes and lived in a way the pioneers were used to. Why Nick liked him so much she would never know.

With no thought to her hypocrisy, Sharon sailed across the room, wearing her brightest smile. 'I was afraid, Mr Caswell, you weren't going to turn up,' she reproached him smilingly.

'In truth I was looking forward to the evening!' Harry fixed her with a biting blue eye. 'You look simply stunning, Miss Russell. Red is undoubtedly your colour.'

'Why, thank you.' Sharon flushed. 'I understand you're trying to get an exhibition together.'

'I'm doing my best.'

'Really, you could have told me,' Katie looked more astonished than hurt.

'It's true,' Harry conceded, shrugging his big shoulders, 'but I wanted it to be a surprise. Who told?'

'Not me!' Nick said mildly, 'I don't do things that way.'

'I must assume it was Ken Thomas. He found his way out to the workshop last week—without any great encouragement on my part. Whatever his limitations as an artist, he never misses a chance to put two and two together.'

'But how sensitive you are!' Sharon cried playfully. 'Didn't you intend to tell anyone at all?'

'Nick knew.' Harry gazed at her, 'but I was waiting to tell Katie myself.'

'I'm thrilled about it anyway.' Katie's expression cleared slightly. 'I even like to think I influenced your decision.'

'You know you did, Kate.' Harry looked down at his big hands. 'Suppose you bring Renee out to the studio.'

'Are you asking me to forgive you?' Katie contemplated him blandly.

'Believe me, it was going to be a big surprise. That's why I told you I wasn't free when you rang me.'

'All right, then, I forgive you.'

'I'll be delighted to come, Mr Caswell,' Renee smiled.

'Won't you please call me Harry?'

'Thank you.'

'The most beautiful young woman I've ever seen!' he exclaimed suddenly, as though moved by some artistic inspiration. 'I made my name as a sculptor,' he said, frowning at her. 'That face has given me an idea. When I see you again, I'll show you a few sketches. Come and see me with Katie, as soon as you're free.'

'Well, I think that's the limit!' Sharon laughed. 'Don't *I* deserve to be sculpted?'

Nick didn't allow Harry time to counter. 'Are you

sure we could allow him to exhibit it?' he asked smilingly. 'Some of the best sculptures are nudes and no one can deny your seductiveness. Renee on the other hand suggests more the classical young goddess timelessly chaste.'

'That's it exactly!' Harry nodded his head in vigorous agreement. 'The vision is everything. I'm thinking in terms of a life size bronze. I haven't done anything worthwhile in ages, but something about Renee has fixed an idea in my mind.'

'The don't-touch-me expression?' Nick suggested suavely.

'The way you said it, a very young goddess who is not allowed to leave her marble temple.'

'Oh, isn't it just thrilling?' Sharon glanced across at Renee and smiled. 'But how are you going to endure all the sittings?'

'Quite well!' Renee laughed involuntarily, 'but what happens if I come down to earth in the middle of them?'

'Perhaps it's what you need,' Nick said dryly. 'Now may I remind you that you've got to dance with me at least once tonight.' He took her hand while they watched him and in a minute more he had drawn her out on to the verandah.

Dancing with Nick turned out to be the mistake of her life. As he drew her to him she didn't speak. Couldn't speak, because she knew it wouldn't sound natural. Philip was frankly staring at them from the door, his eyes following them as they moved into the sweeping shadows.

'Why have you got your eyes closed?' Nick asked her.

'I'm sure I don't know,' she said guardedly. 'I've never enjoyed dancing.'

'So now you're tormented when you do?'

'I seem to betray myself very easily.'

'There's even a melody in the way you tremble. Why have you put your hair up?'

'For the heat,' she said, and drove herself to look at him. 'Don't you like it?'

'I do,' he returned silkily, 'but I prefer it falling around your face, preferably wreathed with flowers. A woman's hair can throw a net around a man.'

'Not you. You'd make a very unwilling captive.'

'Let's talk it out.'

'No.' Close to his body, her heart was racing. Everything about him pleased her senses, the sight, the sound, the clean male fragrance, yet she knew a shiver of fear. Not the fear of recoil, but the fear of breaking her pattern. She had never in her life sought intimacy and coming sensually alive could hurt her. She even shook her head so a shining blonde strand fell forward over her cheekbone.

'At least you're letting me hold you,' he murmured. 'Close your eyes again if you want to.'

Renee felt shaky and secure all at the same time. His hand didn't move up and down on her like Philip's had. It held her with easy mastery, but no attempt at provocation. She wished she could lean against him; wished there was some way for her to relax, but something strange was happening to her, something that could only make her life harder.

'Will you do something for me?' she asked too brightly.

'Of course.' He looked down at her, a faint smile on the fine curve of his mouth.

'I'm afraid I've done the wrong thing again. Philip asked me to spend the day with him tomorrow and I was foolish enough to compromise you.'

'I don't mind.' Nick laughed beneath his breath. 'I take it he was going too fast for you.'

'It was a spur-of-the-moment thing,' she tried to explain. 'Of course if you're doing something ... if you have something arranged....'

'No, tomorrow would be perfect. We'll have lots of conversation.'

'I think you must have wanted to be a psychiatrist,' she said rather tautly.

'Look at me, Renee.'

Something in his low tone filled her with flame. She turned up her head, her delicate face full of unwanted colour, the pupils of her green eyes dilated. 'Come on, admit it, you think I'm odd.'

'I like all sorts, really,' he countered her tolerantly.

'*Don't* you?' she persisted, one white hand on his shoulder.

'There are certain deep-seated tensions in you, Renee. For that matter a lot of people have them, but you're young enough to benefit from a little help.'

Tears leapt into her eyes, making them glitter like jewels, and in an instant he drew her hard against him, turning her so his dark head and wide shoulders blocked the light. 'Don't cry,' he said, almost harshly.

'I can see you mind terribly.'

'Worse than that.'

Her nerves seemed to be strung to breaking point.

Little shivers were passing over her body and he had to feel them because she seemed to be fused to him, unable to direct her own body.

'Please let me go,' she begged.

'I will, when you're steady.' He turned her slightly into the light. She looked beautiful and vulnerable and more than a little lost, but at least she had conquered her tears.

'Where would you like to go tomorrow?' he asked.

'I don't know.' She sounded bewildered, resting almost fully in his arms, like a flower unfolding.

'All right,' he clicked his tongue, 'I'll arrange something.'

'Will you be asking Sharon?' she asked suddenly as though she had just thought of something.

'Nobody else but you would have thought of that, Renee!' There was mockery and amusement in his dark face, his strange eyes lit to silver.

'I just thought you might. . . .'

'Like to hold her hand? A delightful thought, but no, not tomorrow, Renee. If you're as good as you say you are, we'll go riding.'

'Oh, lovely!' She drew back from him with a smile, succeeding in looking very young and happy.

'Are you smiling at me, then,' he gave her an odd amused glance, 'or is it the thought of my horses?'

'Horses are miracles of nature,' she answered seriously. 'I love them.'

'Oh, dear, dear me, there's my answer.'

Apparently it didn't irk him, for his dark face was alive with amusement. Still smiling, he propelled her gently through one of the French doors and a few minutes later supper was served.

Renee found herself heaping a plate along with the others, but she wasn't in the least hungry. The food was superb and so beautifully presented it was easy to pay tribute to Nick's housekeeper, but she could only manage a mouthful or two. Philip had reappeared at her side, looking somewhat strained, and out of the corner of her eyes, she saw Sharon join Nick at the buffet, taking it for granted he would want to have supper with her.

Renee didn't in the least mind. Everything seemed to be happening too swiftly, and she desperately needed a breathing space. Sharon had the sophistication to handle a man like Nick Garbutt, but he put her in a confused tumult. When Philip asked if he could join her, she smiled at him in unconscious relief, then the two of them moved back towards the huge entertainment area at the rear of the house where tables and chairs had been set up around the beautifully lit pool and back on to the grass.

Harry and Katie saw them coming, and Katie lifted a hand to indicate that they were to come and join them. Philip came to a momentary halt, his face betraying his crushed hopes for a tête-à-tête, but Renee took a grateful little breath and smiled.

'Let's go and join them. I haven't had a chance to talk to Mr Caswell properly.'

CHAPTER FOUR

THEY were very late stirring the next morning. Harry had driven them back to the farmhouse, coming in to finish Katie's bottle of champagne, and they had talked on for at least another hour, finding so much of mutual interest Katie didn't even have to ask her niece what she thought of her gifted friend and fellow artist. It had been a wonderful party and both Harry and Katie were night people, at their sparkling best, when others were dead on their feet.

Renee was up first, so she made the breakfast and carried it in on a tray to Katie's room, feeling rather proud of her efforts. She had even picked a rosebud and put it in a lovely little greyed-blue pottery vase and set it down on the lace mat. The pile of scrambled eggs she had ladled into a covered entree dish, the toast was piping hot, and she was gradually mastering the art of making a good cup of tea. Katie was very particular about her tea and she hadn't forgotten the strainer.

'Wake up, sleepyhead!'

'It's not morning, surely?' Katie lifted her ruffled head and directed a smile at her niece.

'If you will stay up all hours drinking champagne.' Noiselessly Renee crossed the room and put the tray down on the table. 'Come on, this is nice and hot.'

'Lovely. You're a good girl.' Languidly, Katie reached for her robe, a gorgeous Japanese kimono, and shouldered into it. 'I'm glad I'm not joining you today, I'll just go sit in the shade.'

'Isn't Harry coming over?'

'This afternoon.' Katie pulled a comb through her hair and pulled a face at her familiar reflection. 'Oh, to look like you!'

'You look well enough.' Renee smiled back. 'I like your Harry.'

'Ah, darling,' Katie seemed to sigh, then seated herself on the floral chintz-covered sofa that faced the low table and matched the two armchairs on the other side. 'Harry makes me ache a little, but I have to ignore it. He values our friendship, but there's nothing very exciting or feminine about me. I've seen a picture of his poor little wife who died. He loved her and I think he's still lonely for her.'

'What was she like?' Renee asked compassionately.

'Beautiful—quite beautiful—and very brave. Harry loves beauty and he's grieved long and hard for her. He's even sought isolation.'

'Drink your juice,' Renee said gently, and sat down in an armchair. 'I'm really sorry, Katie, but are you quite sure Harry doesn't need you?'

'As a wife?' For a second Katie's lips trembled, then she set them firmly. 'I've never allowed myself that hope, darling. Grandma used to tell me if I waited long enough the right man would come along for me, but now I've finally met him most of my life has been used up, and Harry lives too much in the past.'

'Maybe Harry's been waiting for another good woman he could love.' Renee drank her juice quickly, because her throat was tight. 'It seems to me he takes much pleasure from your company. He was really annoyed with Sharon for breaking the news about his showing.'

'She did it deliberately.' Katie helped herself to the scrambled eggs. 'She's a pretty girl, Sharon, and she's greatly repaid her father's training, but she's just that bit bitchy. I'm quite sure she's not right for Nick either, but he seems to admire her.'

'She plays the hostess very well,' Renee pointed out mildly.

Katie shrugged. 'What did you think of Philip?'

'He's very unsure of himself.'

'You know he fancies he's fallen madly in love with you?'

'Don't talk such nonsense, Katie!'

'It's true, dear, and you'd better stop it.'

'That's what Nick said.' Renee put down her fork.

'Oh?' Katie looked up and smiled. 'Right on the ball, is Nick. You know you're going to make Sharon's Sunday a misery?'

'In what way?'

'Silly girl!' Katie chuckled. 'You don't think she's going to love you for taking Nick away from her for a single day?'

'He said he wasn't doing anything else.' Renee looked agitated.

'Well, don't be surprised if she turns up on Emerald. You mentioned in front of Philip that you'd be going riding and Sharon will rush straight home and get out her riding gear. Never mind, she hasn't been invited. Everything is okay in love and war.'

Renee was to remember that when Nick braked the station wagon in front of Emerald homestead, for there on the verandah was Sharon with Philip beside her, both of them in immaculate riding gear.

'Hi!' Sharon moved down the stairs, the sunlight bright on her vivid face. 'Pip told me you were going riding, so I thought why not make up a party? It will be so much fun.'

'Hello there.' Renee smiled, not allowing the faintest trace of amusement or regret to show in her face though she felt both.

'What a good idea!' Nick said dryly. 'I thought you didn't like it much?'

Sharon gave a little smiling frown. 'Don't be naughty, Nick. I think I can stay in the saddle as long as Renee here. I don't imagine she's anything wonderful.'

Renee smiled but didn't answer, turning her blonde head as Philip lounged down the stairs to join them. 'Hope you don't mind, Nick? I mean, Sharon thought it would be quite all right.'

'Sure.' Nick didn't hesitate. 'There are plenty of horses.'

'Nothing too frisky for me,' Philip coughed. 'I can just about hang on.'

'So why did you come?' Renee asked, merely looking interested.

'To see *you*, as it happens.'

'I believe you did ask,' Nick glanced at Renee with enigmatic eyes. 'Well, now we're all here, I say, let's go!'

For Renee's benefit they did the grand tour, with Nick showing her all the valuable animals that would soon join the racing circuit. The whole stables complex was beautifully laid out and a lot of capital had been invested in making it a showplace. There were plenty of grooms and stable hands around and Nick introduced her to his manager and foreman, both pleasant conscientious men with an air of reliability and obviously dedicated to horses.

Despite her astonishing talents in other directions Sharon soon showed she was plainly no horsewoman, neither did she look particularly well in jodhpurs, being rather short-legged. Still, Renee considered, no man would be averse to a few curves and her silk blouse revealed the golden swell of her breasts in a most satisfactory manner. Renee smiled to herself, feeling no edge of triumph in her own ability or the fact that with her slender height she looked extremely elegant in riding gear. Neither did she tire of looking at horses as Sharon and Philip did. They were such beautiful, proud animals it was a delight to inspect them, and she even had the impulse to jump on a particular filly's back.

'You wouldn't consider selling her?' she smiled at Nick and gently stroked the chestnut neck.

'Have you twenty-five thousand handy?'

'*Twenty-five!*' She drew in her breath.

'Well, twenty to you.'

'Stop teasing her, Nick,' Sharon said a little impatiently. 'The fact is, Renee, the filly when she races will probably win a fortune. Her family on both sides have race records.'

'If you're here long enough, Renee, I'll take you to a race meeting,' Nick promised.

'I'd like that.' She smiled at the stable hand who led the filly away. 'It must be wonderful to be an owner.'

'Oh, great!' Sharon seemed to laugh at her. 'If you've had enough of admiring the horseflesh, maybe we can get up on one.'

'I'm sorry!' Renee hadn't intended to apologise, but she had. The sun was striking the chestnut's coat and it gleamed so richly she couldn't tear her eyes away.

'You're not in the least afraid of horses, are you?' Nick asked abruptly.

'Should I be?' She looked up at him in surprise.

'A lot of people are. It pays to have a healthy respect for thoroughbred animals. They're high strung and temperamental and they command a lot of power.'

'I guess they like me,' she confessed.

'They must. The filly didn't flinch from the touch of your hand.'

'Have you done much riding?' Philip came to life to ask.

'Not half as much as I'd like.'

'You look wonderful in riding clothes.' Philip's hazel eyes slipped over the length of her body.

'One has to make a show!' Sharon said gaily. 'Don't worry, Renee, Nick will find us a couple of nice quiet little mares.'

'I've already picked out Renee's mount.' Amusement showed in the curve of Nick's mouth. He turned his dark head and lifted his voice to give the order to some unseen stable hands. 'Bring the horses out.'

Four horses emerged from the big barn, led by two slim-bodied half-caste boys. All of them were handsome, especially the splendid big black, but Renee knew immediately which one she wanted. She even took a few steps forward.

'Just a moment, you're going too fast!' Sharon called sharply.

'May I have the grey, please, Nick?' Renee hadn't even registered Sharon's tone. 'She's so *beautiful*! Look at her lovely delicate head and her soft eyes!'

'She has a temper,' he warned.

'Who hasn't?' she retorted. 'I absolutely *must* have her.'

'All right, then!' he narrowed his silver eyes. 'I'm assuming you know how to handle her.'

'You're assuming a lot, aren't you, Nick?' Sharon's dark eyes flashed her disapproval. 'She could take a nasty spill.'

But Renee had already made her way to the grey, speaking soothingly to the animal, and in another minute she was up on its back, her green eyes so excited they were sparkling with life. 'What's her name?'

'Stardust.'

'How are you, Stardust?' Confidently Renee leaned down and spoke to the attentive mare.

'Look at her, she likes it!' Philip laughed. 'Do you always talk to horses?'

'Of course.' Renee seemed taken aback by the question, and even the mare tossed her head with its beautiful silver mane.

Nick moved to give Sharon a leg up on to a more placid-looking bay and Philip turned a little reluctantly to study his mount carefully. 'I'm glad I'm not riding that black devil!'

'You couldn't!' the stable boy grinned. 'Cyrus is Mr Nick's horse.'

'I wouldn't dare to mount him,' Philip insisted, but accepted a leg up on to the bright bay that stood so calmly to receive its rider.

Renee's grey was moving restlessly as though anxious to be away and Nick spoke to the stable hands, then vaulted into the saddle, tilting his Stetson further over his eyes. 'Come on, then, let's have a look at Emerald.'

As they rode away from the complex Renee carried on a constant conversation with her horse, and the mare was so intelligent, Renee was sure she understood every word of it. It was a wonderful feeling to be in the saddle again and the countryside was so beautiful she felt as though she had cast all her shackles aside.

Out on the open savannah the restlessness and the repression that had simmered in her for so long broke loose. She drew a deep breath, laid her head along the neck of the mare and gave Stardust her head.

They flew. They were actually flying, leaving everyone behind. It was magical, the feeling of release, of being totally unchecked. Pure pleasure. Her hat was hanging down her back by its halter and her hair had whipped free of its gold clasp so it flew behind her in an ash-gold banner. The whole world was beautiful and bright, as fresh as the morning, the wind in her face carrying the scent of boronia that grew all along the river banks.

She didn't even glance back when she heard the thunder of hooves, then the black stallion flashed by her, its powerful legs stretched to the limit, forging ahead and holding the lead. Swift as the mare was, and as full of heart, she didn't have the stallion's speed or stamina, so gently Renee began to rein the mare in until gradually their wild exciting gallop dropped naturally into a canter, then a trot, and she was able to rein in almost by Nick's side.

'I can hardly believe it!' His silver eyes swept her transformed face. She looked ecstatic, a wonderously beautiful creature, so warm and alive it seemed some restraint had been lifted from her.

'That was marvellous!' The excitement still spurted through her so her eyes played over his face in return, lingering on his mouth again, always surprising her with the delight it gave her. 'Well, here we are, but where are the others?' she laughed.

'I'm afraid they can't match you.'

'*Us*.' She laughed again, not herself at all, but someone of spirit and temper and—God help her—passion. She wanted to be alone with him. She wanted him to kiss her. It was crazy!

'Keep on talking,' he coaxed her. 'Right now, this minute, you'd let me make love to you.'

'*No!*'

'Why bother to deny it? Just a minute in time when you're without your resistance.'

'You're hypnotising me,' she said.

'It's the sun on your head.' He leaned forward and crammed her wide-brimmed hat on her long shining hair. 'What a baby!'

'You do make me feel reborn.' Why was she saying it, yet she was filled with sweetness, a melting sensation that gave her face a sheen of soft wonder.

'It was so damned good of Sharon and Philip to join us,' he said in a dry, laconic drawl.

'I thought it would make you happy.'

'Did you, green eyes? Why?'

'Well, I did sort of trick you into this ride.'

'Liar!'

She jerked her head away, not knowing how to handle the urgency she felt in herself. 'They're coming,' she said in a small brittle voice.

'Time to go back into your shell.'

'It's simpler,' she said.

'But I'm not going to let you.'

'You're a pair of beauts, you are!' Sharon called to them.

'I couldn't resist it.' Renee was aware of the other girl's carefully concealed anger.

'Are you always so impulsive?' Philip asked in his soft voice.

'I love to gallop,' she smiled. 'It's just an obsession.'

'We had no idea you could ride so well,' Sharon said. 'As a matter of fact you might have told us.'

'What on earth for?' Nick moved to her side. 'You look hot. Are you sure you're going to enjoy this?'

'As long as Renee doesn't do that galloping bit again,' Sharon gave a thin smile, 'though I suppose it is fun to show off.'

'That, honey, is too absurd!' Nick pushed Sharon's hat over her eyes. 'You know nothing about a rider's exuberance, you're more like a pussy cat warm on the front mat.'

'Just let me ride with you.' Sharon fixed her hat and looked up at him with glowing dark eyes, a golden bloom on her skin and her throat and the tantalising swell of her breasts.

'O.K. Rein along beside me quietly. We'll keep near the river where there's plenty of shade.'

The excitement was over, but the rest of the day was a mixture of many things; a new world full of unfamiliar sights and sounds, cattle moving, grazing, at rest in the shade, the green dreaming beauty of the river, sunlight filtered through trees. It was big, so big they could never ride to the ends of it, and to the north and north east the rain forest rose like a massive green canopy keeping in check the great holding.

The birds flew and flurried about them in clouds of colour, cockatoos, parrots and rainbow birds, and Nick told her how the brolgas performed their ritual ballets every so often down by the lagoons. The lagoons themselves were of surpassing beauty, shadowed by trees and floating many kinds of lilies through blue-violet to creamy white. But while her eyes were constantly being beguiled, her pleasure was somewhat blurred by forever having Philip's quiet voice in her ear. He kept beside her relentlessly, not bothersome because she felt, in a way, sorry for him, but clinging to the point where she felt like galloping away again.

Sharon was all sweetness now, with Nick at her side, and her pert vivid face gave the impression that she was having a wonderful time. It was then so much more of a shock when she showed her claws. They had returned to the homestead and were freshening up before having a cool drink when Sharon launched into what was troubling her.

'Will you do one thing for me, Renee?'

'Why, certainly.' Renee put her comb down and turned away from the mirror.

'Remember Nick's mine.'

'Please. . . .'

'Oh, don't give me that soft little girl look,' Sharon made a little laughing face. 'Be honest with me, now, he attracts you.'

'Perhaps a little! He's a very attractive man,' purposefully Renee kept her voice light. 'But I can't do you any harm, Sharon, I have too many other things on my mind.'

'Such as? You're something of a mystery, aren't you?' Sharon touched her glossy curls lightly.

'Only to myself,' Renee returned almost casually, 'It's been a lovely day!'

Sharon laughed charmingly. 'Well, you certainly made it for Pip. Since Mother died he's gone away some place in his mind, but you have that soft touch he seems to like. We must make a date for dinner this week. I'd like to show you our place. We've had it redecorated and it looks rather special. Not Emerald, of course, but nice enough to invite our friends.'

Without waiting for Renee's answer, she went to the door and put her hand on the knob. 'I'll run along and help Nick with the drinks. See you on the terrace. I might even take a swim—I leave my gear here.' For an instant her black eyes looked directly into Renee's and the message they carried couldn't have been clearer. Hands off. He's mine!

A few days later Renee met Ken Thomas, the artist, for the first time. He'd been down in Brisbane, he explained, seeing his agent, otherwise he would have loved to have come to her party. He had driven up to the farmhouse that afternoon while Katie was busy putting the finishing touches to Nick's 'The River Track' and now he was lounging comfortably in one of the planter's chairs begging Renee to lower herself into a seat beside him.

'What do you think of our wild North?' he asked her.

For a young man he had a somewhat jaded look, but he was trying very hard to be nice to Renee.

'I love it!' She moved gracefully and sank into a

chair. 'Even the heat, though it does make me a little languid.'

'You'll get used to it if you stay long enough. How long are you staying anyway?' His sherry-coloured eyes sharpened, shades lighter than his hair and the droopy moustache that merged into a beard.

'Oh, a little longer,' Renee tilted her head back, 'I'm sort of wrestling with a few problems.'

'I'll bet it's a man.' He gave a dry little laugh.

'More than that,' she sighed. 'One feels goaded sometimes. Goaded beyond endurance.'

The sherry eyes traced the lovely outline of her profile. 'That's all nonsense, you know. Why don't you just take off?'

'There's no profit in running away from life. I'd like to be strong enough to face it. But don't let's talk about me, Katie tells me you're becoming very successful.'

'Don't you mean, sweetie, my work *sells*?'

'I must confess I've never seen any of it.'

'You must be haunting the wrong galleries. I'm not in Katie's class, never will be, but there's a market for what I do, and the price is right. Besides, it's a nice life. I've always been reluctant to work and this comes nice and easy. Katie thinks it's all rather terrible, but she's too kind to say so. Caswell is somewhat abrasive, but Nick Garbutt's the cruel one. He just took one look and those icy eyes of his said it all. I'm sure you've seen the Garbutt collection. Not that I care a damn about what Nick thinks or any other man.'

'Well, I'd like to see your work,' she said consolingly, seeing the pulse that beat in his temple.

'And you shall. What about now?' His sherry eyes

sparkled at her and for the first time she became aware of his charm. A raffish charm certainly, but it was there.

'Well, I don't know....' She looked back into the house uncertainly.

'Oh, come on now, surely you don't need a chaperone? I'm only taking you to my studio. We'd be there and back in an hour.' He suddenly held out his hand to her. 'Come on, Renee, let's go and gloat over them. Exotic stuff people like to hang on their walls.'

'I'll have to tell Katie.'

'She won't mind when the muse is on her.'

'I don't think she will. Just give me a few moments.'

Katie gave a dry little chuckle when Renee told her Ken had asked her to see his work. 'Go along, darling, but don't be disappointed.'

'I rather like him,' Renee admitted.

'So do I, but he's a cocky young devil. He even made a play for Sharon at one time. Now they're deadly enemies.'

'How could anyone compare with Nick,' she said unguardedly.

'H'm!' Katie gave another one of her delicious little chuckles, but her blue eyes sharpened. 'I wondered what you thought of him.'

'Oh, Katie!'

'Funny child. Run along then and enjoy yourself. If you only live for the day Ken's good company.'

When they arrived at length at his little hideaway studio, Renee was almost too numb to appreciate it. Ken Thomas was easily the worst driver she had ever been with, not in the reckless sense, but in his sheer lack of feeling for his tired little car. The cars she was used to purred, so she could look out of the window and enjoy the scenery, but Ken's manner of driving and the protesting rattles and groans of the motor gave the impression he was doing battle. At least nothing terrible could really happen, for the little car had no power at all, or it had been driven so hard it was fed up.

It was a comfort to open the door and slide out into the sunshine.

'There, that didn't take long!' Ken ran his hand through his thick, tawny hair.

'Lordy!' Renee looked at him and laughed. 'At least let me drive back. I don't mind in the least changing gear.'

'Now, now, don't be naughty. I know I've no feeling for machinery. But come with me to my castle.'

'It's very picturesque!'

'Just a shack, darling, but I think it's beautiful!'

'Did you build it?' Renee looked at the simple box-like wooden construction that was made so appealing by all the tropical profusion of trees and shrubs and flowering vines.

'God, no! The only callouses I get are from a paint-brush. One of the carpenters in the town knocked it up for me. Perhaps it'll stand in a cyclone. We'll soon know.'

The front door wasn't locked, Renee noticed, and he stood back to allow her to cross his threshold.

It was almost theatrical, everything was so radiantly coloured. 'Very trendy!' she said kindly.

'It's comfortable,' he answered cheerfully, 'and when I want to change my mood I just slap some fresh paint all over the walls.'

'How exciting!'

'No sense in having the professional designers in,' he grinned. 'Dear Sharon, now, set out to advise me. I believe I created just this atmosphere to spite her.'

'You don't like her?' Renee was trying desperately to find some cohesive scheme in the long, open room.

'I don't know,' Ken returned rather flatly, 'At one time I thought myself terribly in love with her, but she's a real bitch.'

'In what way?' Renee picked up a wooden elephant painted red and put it down again.

'The way she digs money and the big time. You've seen the way she runs after Garbutt. Take off, Thomas, I'm going to marry a millionaire.'

'Did she actually say that?' Renee sounded doubtful.

'I'll say, and more. She's becoming desperate, you know. Another six months and she'll be an old maid. She's my age.'

'Twenty-eight?'

'Twenty-nine,' Ken said gloomily. 'She doesn't know it, but she's got herself one big problem. She's known Nick all her life and don't think *his* life hasn't been complicated with women, yet he hasn't married a one of them. Perhaps someone will come along right out of the blue, but until that time Sharon is going to live in hopes. She's got this hero complex and she's convinced she could make Nick a wife to be proud of.'

'From what I've seen, she seems perfect for the role!' Renee moved suddenly to study some sea shells set out on a table.

'Oh, hell, let's forget her. Just thinking about her ruins my good humour. The studio is out the back— it's best for the light. Would you like tea or coffee, I'm forgetting my manners.'

'Coffee would be fine, if you're ready for it now?'

'I really came up to the farmhouse to spirit you away,' he confessed with a mocking grin. 'I don't think Katie approves of me.'

'Wrong, she likes you.' Renee followed him from the room.

'I said *approve*, sweetie. Also she thinks my work is muck.'

'What do you think?' Renee halted at the doorway to the studio and looked at him seriously.

'I know I can do better, but it's not easy. If I try something else I might finish up poor and under-nourished. This way, at least, I'm making a living.'

'Perhaps in time you'll be free to do what you want,' Renee offered gravely.

'You're nice, aren't you?' He gave her a searching glance. 'I mean, you're a really nice girl. Kind. I thought all women were basically the same—real bitches.'

'Perhaps you've been treated badly.'

'When I first came up here, Sharon was quite different, warm and friendly, now she's perfected this high, bold, superior manner as befitting the future mistress of Emerald. As for that sely-pitying brother of hers——!'

'He's not such a bad fellow!' Renee protested.

'You mark my words, he'll give some woman a dreadful life—always wincing and whining and making snide remarks. His mother's fault, of course. She simply babied him until the day she died. At least Sharon has spunk and she's got a good brain. Got it from the old man, of course Cy is a good sort.' With a flourish, Ken threw open the door and waved her in. 'Don't be afraid to say what you think.'

'I'm no authority.'

'Perhaps not, sweetie, but you're used to quality. It's written all over you. You're positively beautiful, like a chaste Grecian goddess.'

'Wait until you get to know me. I'm very human.'

'Really?' He gave a mock leer. 'No, seriously, Renee, you can trust me. I'm not really a ladies' man, though you'll hear a lot to the contrary. Now, why don't you sit here and I'll set up some of my best on an easel. If you really want to fall flat on your face with respect wait until you see Harry's. He's a genius, that man. He even lets me pinch a few of his ideas.'

'He wants to sculpt my head,' Renee said a little vaguely, working at clearing a space for herself.

'Does he really?' Ken straightened with a canvas in his hand. 'What, a bronze?'

'A life-size head, I believe.'

'What's got into him? He's been stagnating for years. And with all that God-given ability!'

'It isn't easy to answer for anyone else. I suppose in a way he must be sheltering from life. I understand he was devoted to his wife and she died tragically.'

'Come, come, that was years ago!'

'Some feel more deeply than others, perhaps. Now let me see that painting, if I may?'

'You asked for it, kiddo. There are plenty. Plenty!'

In the end, Renee wasn't all that disappointed. In fact, some of them she quite liked if they could have been toned down a little. Ken had caught the vibrancy and lushness of the tropics, the sense of being in a different world, but it seemed to Renee everything would be much better if he didn't try so hard to make a brave show of it.

'Well, come on, you've been peering at them long enough,' Ken muttered a little anxiously.

'Some aspects of your work are excellent, surely?' she said.

'Are you asking me or telling me?'

'A lot here I like, Ken, but I suspect you're trying to please the less discerning public.'

'I've already admitted that. It's disgusting, isn't it, the whole lot!' Ken put his head between his two hands.

'I think you can do much, much better and very easily too. It's easy for me to talk, I've been raised with a silver spoon in my mouth, but I think you could win through if you followed your own vision. You *can* paint.'

'Thank you. Even Harry's told me that, but of course I start wanting to earn money.'

'As well you might!' Renee smiled at him. 'One can't do without the rotten stuff.'

'So there it is, you don't like them?'

'I didn't say that at all!' Renee began to walk around the room again. 'Look at this,' she held up a small canvas. 'This is really good.'

'Except it didn't sell.'

'I'll buy it myself. And another thing, do more like this and take them to another gallery. You can't stay in the same place. You have to move up one.'

'Who am I fighting for, sweetie?'

'For yourself!' She looked at him, surprised. 'As *I* should be doing.'

'You don't have to buy that!' Gently Ken took the

canvas off her. 'It's a gift. So are you, for that matter. I suppose I could manage for a while on what I've saved up. And don't go telling Katie.'

'I won't. Thanks, Ken. If you really mean it about the painting, I'll treasure it.'

'I think it might even surprise your dear aunt. To what degree I don't know, but it will surprise her.'

'Incidentally,' added Renee, 'did you tell Sharon about Mr Caswell's showing?'

'I did *not*!' Ken came to a surprised halt.

'I wonder how she found out?'

'Well, *I* didn't tell her,' Ken protested. 'I mean I knew Harry was keeping it a secret and God knows I don't want him to bar me from his workshop.'

'I'm sorry,' said Renee.

'No, that's all right. I haven't even seen Sharon. And if you want to know that was one good reason why I didn't come to the party on Emerald. I'd have had to fight off the impulse to cry, or I'd have made a terrible fool of myself.'

'Let's have some coffee,' Renee said soothingly.

'I just hope I can dig up something to go with it.'

Ken did allow her to drive back to the farmhouse and treated more gently, the little car responded with surprisingly good manners. True to what Katie had said of him, Ken was good company, but Renee considered he deserved to be treated more seriously by everyone, including himself. His life hadn't been easy, the only son of a widowed mother, who herself had died when he was in his early teens. From then on, he had drifted around the countryside without benefit of more schooling, taking any job he could find. In addition, he had suffered from severe asthma, which miraculously went away, in his own words, 'as soon as I went bush and started to paint.'

When Renee suggested it might have been emotional, he hadn't disagreed. She liked him and it seemed he liked her, so they arrived back at the farmhouse laughing, only to have the smiles wiped from their faces as they saw Sharon and Nick standing in the garden, talking to Katie.

'Oh God!' Ken wailed in anguish.

'Don't worry, you just have to say hello and whizz out,' Renee tried to comfort him.

'Why can't I forget her?' Ken hissed quietly. 'I'm weak, weak, *weak*!'

'Poor Ken!'

Nick was watching them with detachment, but it seemed to Renee, for someone with no emotional involvement Sharon was positively glaring at Ken, who had adopted a very jaunty attitude to cover his true feelings.

'Hi there!' His voice crackled with life. 'I'd rather take Renee to see my paintings than anyone else in the world!'

'Really? What *was* your reaction, Renee?' Sharon asked in a somewhat acid tone.

'How are you, Nick?' Renee glanced at Nick quietly, then answered Sharon's question. 'I think Ken could turn out to surprise you.'

'See?' Ken's sherry eyes sharpened. 'She's even examined the condition of my soul.'

'Yuck!'

'Yucky or not, we've enjoyed ourselves, haven't we, Renee?' Ken flung himself round to ask the question.

'Yes,' she answered gently, aware of his private agony.

Sharon was looking very hard and contemptuous, apparently unaware Ken was feeling it deeply. 'I've even been presented with a painting.'

'Let's see it,' Nick suggested idly.

'Of course you can, it's in the car.' Ken walked away from them and returned with the small canvas. 'Renee liked it.'

'Maybe she was just being polite,' Sharon said waspishly.

'No, Sharon, I *liked* it,' Renee corrected her.

'Then let's have a look at it in the right light,' Katie said mildly, her expressive face not giving anything away.

They all walked back up on to the verandah, and Nick propped the painting up on a chair, moving back a few paces to stand beside Katie. 'It had occurred to me that you could do as well as this.'

Ken actually blushed. 'You like it?'

'It's a heap more powerful than what you usually do.'

'I agree.' Katie picked up the small canvas of a storm going away and examined it closely. 'I don't understand you, Ken, if you can paint as well as this, why are you expending so much time and energy on your current style?'

'I've been frequently broke in my life,' he answered dryly, 'so I deliver myself up to a certain market. It's an uneasy feeling not having money coming in.'

'You're just using that for an excuse!' Sharon burst out in a voice charged with feeling. 'The truth is you're too lazy to work hard. This little intellectual exercise is only a flash in the pan. You have to be able to keep it up.'

'Oh God!' Ken lunged away from her and fell into a

chair. 'What a shrew you're turning into!'

'Because I speak the truth?' Sharon turned on him in an ice-cold fury. With her dark eyes flashing she looked superb, and Renee could see Ken was very conscious of it.

'You mustn't mind criticism,' Nick told the younger man dryly. 'If Sharon's unable to accept your sincerity and capacity for work, I suppose you could rise to the challenge. So you won't starve I'm prepared to stake you until you generate enough work for a serious exhibition.'

'How could you be so confident, Nick?' Sharon asked intensely.

'I think that's a wonderful suggestion!' Renee cried with spontaneous warmth.

'I'm so sorry, Renee,' Sharon said thinly, 'but I don't think you know enough about it.'

'Indeed she does,' Katie intervened, and smiled. 'Really, Nick, what would a young artist do without a patron? I must say this picture of Ken's has surprised me, although Harry told me he was wasting a gift.'

'I don't know what to say, Nick!' Ken was still lounging in the chair, looking shocked.

'You understand, of course, I expect results.'

Ken touched his forehead as though he were mildly dazed. 'Just watch me!'

Nick's answer was a slight smile and Ken pulled himself up and suddenly grabbed Renee whirling and twirling her down the length of the verandah. 'You look like an angel, and you are! You've brought me luck. You even persuaded Nick to help me.'

'Stop, you're making me dizzy!'

'Oh, I *love* you!' Ken cried, still waltzing her madly

until Nick caught her at the right moment and held her steady, with one hand on her shoulder.

She stood there a little breathless, smiling, aware without looking that Sharon was upset for some reason.

'If you don't mind, Nick, I should be getting back!' Sharon announced, throwing her glossy head back a little.

'Let me take you,' Ken offered, apparently shocking her. 'I'm going your way, and I'm sure Renee told me, Nick was staying to dinner.'

'*Are* you?' Sharon's voice exploded, sounding highly irritated.

'Of course I have time to take you home,' Nick answered suavely, eyeing Renee impassively.

'Don't bother!' Sharon took a long breath as though to calm herself. 'If Ken's leaving now he might as well run me home. I can't say I'm as sympathetic towards him as you all appear to be.'

'You misjudge me, my lady!' Ken jerked upright, moving hastily to the stairs.

Sharon turned to raise her delicate black eyebrows. 'Remember you're having dinner with us on Wednesday night!' Her glance encompassed Katie and Renee. 'Dad and Philip are so looking forward to it.'

'Perfect!' said Katie.

'I'll see you tomorrow, Nick,' Sharon added, some fire burning in her eyes. 'Thank you very much for the opals. They're absolutely beautiful.'

'And they'll suit you,' Nick smiled. 'See you later, Ken. Ring me towards the end of the week and we'll arrange a time for a serious discussion.'

'Thanks a million, Nick!' Ken suddenly reached out and gave Nick's hand an iron clasp. 'I don't think you're going to regret it.'

'I don't expect to,' Nick answered with quiet authority.

They stood in silence while Ken helped Sharon into his car, his tawny head bent to her glossy curls, then they jolted off, with Honey, the labrador, coming up from the orchard, barking them off.

'I've no idea why Ken said that about you're staying to dinner!' Renee looked up at Nick with wide green eyes.

'At least he was right about our having dinner together.'

'When did you decide that?'

'The minute Katie told me she wanted to entertain Harry alone.'

'I didn't say that, darling,' Katie smiled, 'but if Nick wants to take you off to Emerald, the very least you could do is accept.'

'You don't mind?'

'What a little girl you are, Renee,' Nick's silver eyes mocked her. 'Katie and Harry will manage.'

'I think he really wants to get started on his bronze,' Katie murmured.

'And that's good, considering Harry's been hiding from life too long,' Nick said firmly, 'but there are other times, and I'm sure you don't mind. Right now, I'm taking Renee back to Emerald.'

'May I change?' Renee glanced down at her white cotton slacks, trying desperately to smother her nervous excitement.

'If you want to, but you could earn your living modelling.'

'Wear the green,' said Katie, 'I love you in that.'

CHAPTER FIVE

THEY arrived back at Emerald homestead to find it quiet.

'Martha has gone off on one of her good deeds,' Nick explained. 'A friend has just come out of hospital and needs Martha to support her for a few days.'

'So who's going to get our dinner?'

'Sorry,' he smiled at her, 'didn't I tell you? *You.*'

'Then you'd better not be too critical.'

'Don't worry, I'll help you, but we've got time yet before we start preparations. I want you to get a better idea of how we operate here. Everything seemed to misfire the other day. Neither Sharon nor Philip are particularly interested in station life or being shown horses. You seem to relish it.'

'It's a dream! Plus all the wonderful peace.'

'Enough to renounce the city and all it has to offer?' He stood looking down at her, a mocking glint in his silver eyes.

'It all depends on what one means by the good life. I'm not particularly drawn to the big cities and I've lived there all my life. Also, I'm terrified of crowds. I just want them to go away.'

'Yet you're prepared to sell your life to this Simon?' he taunted her. '*I am* surprised.'

'You think I should go back and tell him he's wasting his time?'

'It's the only way you can take charge of your own

life,' he told her, a slight frown between his winged brows.

'You don't really admire me, do you?' she said a little sadly. 'I suppose it's easy for a man like you to be impatient of other people's inadequacies.'

'And what specifically are yours?' he asked her. 'Put down that ornament and look at me.'

'Maybe I'm frightened of what you'll see.'

'Not quite the same person you were a week ago.' He laid his hand on her shoulder and turned her, feeling rather than seeing the strange excitement that was in her. Tonight she had left her long hair free, a curtain of pale gold around her delicate oval face. 'What is it you want out of life, Renee?'

'To be my own person,' she said quickly, standing perfectly still beneath his hand. 'I don't want any one telling me how to dress, or how to act or whom to marry.'

'Well, that's not a lot ... little things....'

'But they're important. Some people are born to dominate and others to do what they're told. All my life I've been one of them, now I want to be free to make my own choice about everything.'

'Including the man you want to marry—or are you still on the total freedom kick?'

'Aren't you?' She looked up at him with her shimmering eyes, darkened to jade by the depth of colour in her dress.

'I'm willing to take the risk, Renee,' he said lightly, 'the problem is to find a woman to love.'

So love me! Inside she screamed it, and it shocked her. This was something she never wanted to happen. She couldn't handle anything so complicated, so demanding, as love. And there was the real confusion, for her body was expressing its reluctance to follow the dictates of her mind, leaning towards his in an age-old craving.

'Let's go outside, shall we?' she asked breathlessly. 'The light has almost gone and there's so much to see.'

'Of course,' he agreed, but from the sound of his voice he was laughing at her.

For the best part of an hour they roamed the establishment, with Nick answering all her questions in detail. It was exhilarating. It really was, and the staff seemed to stand about grinning indulgently. Not only was she a very beautiful young woman, but she actually seemed to truly love horses. When they returned to the house, she was relaxed and smiling and Nick turned her slowly towards the kitchen and offered her one of Martha's clean aprons.

'We'll try something simple,' he said mildly, and because she was having a little difficulty tied the big apron neatly around her narrow waist smiling a little at the effect over her green silk jersey dress.

'What's simple?' she asked. 'Katie's let me work at making a salad.'

'That will do for a start,' he said dryly. 'It's my belief between the two of us we can make something of you. How about a grill, and there's some tiny new potatoes. Put them on to boil before you make the salad.'

'Yes, Boss!' Renee gave quite a creditable imitation of the black workers' liquid tones.

'What about a drink to make your task easier?'

'Just one, I think,' she said, frowning at the huge refrigerator. 'This is a very big kitchen, isn't it?'

'Martha's domain. As you know, I do a lot of entertaining and I have to keep Martha happy.'

'Most women would find this a dream, but I've just realised I don't know where anything is.'

'Didn't I tell you I'd help you?'

He did, in the process saying some very funny things that delighted her because they didn't fit her preconceived image of all hard, masculine authority without humour. It was her choice to eat out on the rear terrace because it was absolutely blissful to look up at the stars, so big and brilliant they left her breathless with wonder. But above and beyond the stars, Nick's dark face seduced her gaze.

In the softly glimmering light he looked very vivid and compelling, his pale shirt with the buttoned-down pockets throwing his deep tan into stunning relief, his eyes almost the colour of the stars and holding the same magic. Yet their conversation wasn't inconsequential. Renee was an intelligent young woman and she listened seriously while Nick told her of his concern for the rights of the aboriginal people without whom his own pioneering family couldn't have met the challenge of establishing and manning a great station. Even today his top hands were aboriginal stockmen. The 'experts' were the white men, but the devoted workforce and the excellent horsemen were the descendants of the same faithful workers who had called Charles Hunter-Garbutt boss.

'I could listen to you for ever,' she said earnestly.

He shook his head and smiled. 'Enough serious discussion for tonight. Let's go inside. Would you like coffee?'

'You make it and I'll just load the dishes on to the trolley.'

'Mercifully we have Martha's dishwasher!' He rose and came around to hold her chair. 'Well, better get going, little one. May I congratulate you on an excellent salad?'

'I think the dressing had something to do with it.'

'You really are beautiful,' he said abruptly.

'Th-thank you.' Renee was stammering again, the blood leaping to her high cheekbones. All through the meal she had enjoyed so very much, he had never looked at her like *that*. Putting her at risk. As he walked away she took a last swallow of her wine as though it would help her to be bolder, not so soft and vulnerable.

They had coffee in the library and Nick showed her the family diaries, letting her take them into her hands. 'You come from a long line of strong, determined people, don't you?'

'You're right in thinking I take what I want.'

Her heavy lashes fluttered and she caught her breath on a nervous laugh. 'I imagine you might.'

He took the diaries out of her weakened hands and put them down on the great library desk. 'Come over here,' he said, taking her arm and drawing her back towards the long sofa, upholstered in bronze velvet.

'I really should go home, Nick.' She couldn't smooth her voice out. It sounded soft and shaky.

'I'll take you home later.'

Every nerve end was tingling, the trembling of her body, betraying her unspoken thoughts. She had nothing to give a man and soon he would know.

'Please, Nick, it must be getting late!' She was running on stupidly, driven by panic.

'Stop fluttering,' he said tautly, tension in his own

lean, powerful body. 'You've been tormenting me long enough!'

'No, I never meant it!' Her voice was faint, and she tried to jerk away, her beautiful angel's head unconsciously lifted in challenge.

'Your eyes tell the truth!'

And now she was trapped, for he lifted her in his arms with his magnificent strength, bringing them both down on to the sofa with one curiously graceful motion. A monstrous thing and she was already doomed.

'What do you expect, little one, if you throw yourself at me.'

'Please, Nick, you're immune.'

'My poor girl, do you think so? You can't be unaware that I want to kiss you.'

'But I'm cold ... frigid ... an ice-lady!'

'You're none of those things,' he murmured. 'You're beautiful. *Too* beautiful!'

'You don't know, Nick. You can't possibly know.'

'Give me your mouth. I need it.'

She could have been lifted by a wild wind, so swiftly did she respond to his unconcealed command. From the moment she had met him, new forces had been set in motion, now she had to accept the consequences, trembling while he pulled her body hard into his arms, his hand in her blonde hair, a little cruel in the moment of demand.

When his mouth closed over hers, she went rigid, almost shocked out of her mind with the intimate contact.

'*Renee!*' His breath hit her like incense, his hand calming her slender body.

'I can't, Nick,' she whispered against his cleft chin, terrified of her feelings.

'I'm sure you can.'

His voice seemed to be coming from afar off and she was unable to control what was happening. He moved her a little on his shoulder, so he could kiss every inch of her face and throat, teasing her very gently, so she couldn't relax though she was cradled in his arms.

It was so beautiful it was terrible, his mouth moving over her heating her creamy skin. If he touched her breasts, she would die. But he didn't, exploring her face and her throat and her shell-like ears, so she clutched him convulsively, stopping the fiery trail of his mouth.

Kiss me.' She had never begged such a thing in her life, sounded so imperious.

Even as she threw her slender arms about his head she felt the shudder in his body so she opened her mouth instinctively. wanting this awakening as much as she feared it.

'Love me!' Had she said it, or was she only begging with her body, crushed up against him, oblivious of it, desperately trying to satiate an unsatisfied hunger.

'I *want* to!'

She must have said it, for the low answering sound of his voice overwhelmed her. He was remaking her in his own fashion, so she knew for the first time the all-powerful pull of passion.

She wanted to cry. She wanted to touch him. Bare skin, his and hers. She slid her hand into his shirt, feeling the button give, her eyes closed tightly, tracing circles on his skin, liking the tangle of dark hair, the hard strength of his ribs. Everything about him was making her blind with hunger. She had no idea what she was doing, everything was going so fast. . . .

When he broke away from her abruptly, she gasped in protest, her flesh on fire, her green eyes dazed and feverishly bright.

'I've never known a woman like you,' he said huskily, releasing her hands from around his neck.

'I still have the taste of you in my mouth,' she whispered, 'clinging to me.'

'I know.' Determinedly he moved, lifting her to her feet, smoothing her long hair behind her ear, holding her steady. 'Just so you won't hate me in the morning, I'm taking you home—now!'

'It wasn't a game, was it, Nick?' She tilted her head to him, as if she desperately had to know.

'Did it feel like a game?' His glance struck her face, something without name in the brilliance of his eyes and the flare of his nostrils.

'It felt like nothing I've ever experienced in my life!' There was a kind of pain in her soft, muffled voice, but she was still pierced through with emotion.

In the car she was silent, self-conscious now, because he had returned so rapidly to normal, his silver-grey eyes mocking, skimming her averted profile.

'Don't blame yourself for what happened, Renee,' he said dryly.

'I shall never be able to see you again without wanting to run away.'

'Would that help?' A brittle little smile played around his mouth.

'Please, Nick, can't you see I don't want involvement?'

'What do you mean?' he asked with hard cynicism. 'Are you somehow imagining I might trap you into becoming my lover?'

'Oh, Nick, *please*!' Her eyes filled with tears.

'Such an odd mixture you are, Renee!' He kept his eyes intently on the road. 'A green-eyed witch and a Vestal Virgin. I'll have to get you back on my couch as a patient. And don't delude yourself you don't know how to respond to a man. After tonight, you should be glad to throw that idea out of the door.'

'I've never ... ever....'

'I think I'd strangle you if you had.'

'So why did you kiss me, because you thought it would be good therapy?'

'Maybe I've wanted to since I picked you up at the bus depot. There's never been any question in my mind about gentlemen preferring blondes.'

'Funny!' she returned bitterly.

'Don't lose your sense of humour.'

'What about Sharon, or are you getting in all your last flings?' She stared across at him, desire returning in a wave to engulf her.

'How absolutely priceless! You're being bitchy!' His grey eyes glinted with amusement.

'I'm sorry, I really am.' Renee looked away, ashamed of herself. 'I'll even send you a wedding present.'

'Thank you. I've definitely got marriage in mind.'

Only much later, alone in her room and unable to sleep, did she summon up the courage to face her feelings for Nick. She wanted to call it fascination, the drugged kind of rapture, but the answer was too easy. Aside from the violent excitement he aroused in her, something deep inside her reached out for him. He was a strong, thinking, man, highly intelligent, principled and progressive. There was so much that went into making a man like Nick Garbutt.

Staring up at the star, with the breeze lifting her thin nightdress away from her body, she relived the powerful, moving moments she had known in his arms.

'Oh God!' Said like that, it was a prayer. Had she really tempted the fall of fire? From the very first moment she had met him she had known by instinct he would affect her life.

Out in the garden the tall palms were swaying and it gave her an odd sense of vertigo. Too much had happened tonight and maybe she would be punished for it. Nick had taught her in the most exquisitely cruel way possible that she was indeed a woman, with all a woman's needs. But only he held her captive.

She slept fitfully that night and all her dreams were of Nick. Once she woke up, certain she could feel the pressure of his mouth. He seemed to be all around her and she even put out her hand to catch at a tangible presence, but of course he wasn't there. She knew perfectly well he didn't love her, but he had made up his mind to help her somehow. One thing was certain, after such an emotional upheaval, she was not going to be dictated to by her parents. Simon had made her believe things that simply weren't true. She had accepted without argument his claim that she was frigid because she had never known hunger before Nick. Now she was astonished by her own depths even though she knew this self-knowledge could make her desperately unhappy. Whether Nick could care for her or not, Sharon certainly wasn't going to allow her to take Nick away. Sharon adored him and she had hoped for a long time.

In the morning she was pale and quiet, but it apparently suited Harry Caswell quite well. Katie drove Renee over to Harry's ramshackle paradise, stayed for a cup of coffee then, went on her way, promising to return about lunch time. Her own work was waiting for her and besides, Harry wasn't going to let her stay anyway.

The studio was separate from the simple wooden house, just across the garden and overhung with the beautiful blossoming trees of the tropics. Harry let her wander around at her leisure, exclaiming over the open shelves filled with pottery for the firing, magnificent finished pieces, and bench after bench covered with half-formed and complete wax figures. The whole room appeared to be in a state of controlled chaos, with coloured plastic buckets, tins of paint, hand-drills, armatures, a vice and saw, tins, bottles, jars, books piled high, or strewn over the tables, and dominating one end of the light-filled room, a wonderful bronze of a woman holding her hair back from her face.

'How lovely!' Renee went to stand before it. It was life-size, standing on a block, a beautiful face and a beautiful nude body, faithfully recorded with a wonderful grace. It wasn't a voluptuous figure, neither was it idealised, but an immensely moving, sensuous portrayal of a slight, high-breasted nymph.

'My wife,' Harry said tonelessly.

'It's superb!'

For a minute Harry didn't answer. 'She often used to model for me. This is the best thing I've ever done —unique. I'll never part with it.'

'She looks so young.'

'Twenty-three. I sculpted this in the early days of our marriage. She was dead before she was forty.'

'I'm so sorry, Harry,' Renee let her eyes stray to his face. 'You must have suffered.'

'It *was* a strain, both mentally and physically, but Beth kept me going. Right to the end, she was the strong one. I've never forgotten.'

'And she's here.'

'Of course she is!' Harry said almost curtly.

'I understand how you feel, Harry,' the words came quickly as she instinctively tried to comfort him.

'How could you, you're so young? You don't know what it's like to be left alone and desolate. When Beth died, I died too. That's what it felt like.'

Almost blindly Harry reached out and touched the bronze cheeks, the beautiful moulded mouth. 'Beth was an artist in her own right, but she gave up everything for me. She always said I had the greater gift and she was happy just serving it. Then she died.'

Renee nodded and moved closer to his arm. 'Yet you had a great love. It's not given to everyone. Your Beth would want you to be happy and continue with your work.'

'So I do after a fashion. It was easy to turn to pottery, but sculpture was my first love. Katie is forever badgering me to go back to it. She's a wonderful woman, your aunt. I've been blessed with her friendship.'

But she wants more, Renee thought, stricken by a sense of defeat for Katie. In that single gesture, far more than his words, Harry had revealed the depth of feeling he still had for his dead wife.

'Well,' Harry turned away abruptly from the sculpture, 'all of this must be very depressing for you. I don't want it to be that. I have my good days when my memories aren't so painful, and the incredible thing is Katie's niece has supplied me with some long-needed inspiration. You have a wonderful face, very tender and trusting, and of course, those beautiful bones. The long hair has given me another idea. I think I'll just drape it around your throat. It flows naturally over the contours of your head. Sit down, child, in that chair.'

'This one?' Renee lifted some magazines.

'That's right.' Harry was moulding some wax in his huge hands. 'I want this to be a poetic image, but strong. There's delicacy in your face, but there's also a latent strength. Fine planes of cheek and jaw ... those beautiful high cheekbones!' From sadness and pain, his voice had gone to a kind of professional exultance. 'Now, when you get too bored sing out!'

Time passed, and Harry didn't even notice her slump in her chair. With so few hours of sleep her eyelids were heavy. Now and again, she remarked his expression, the lighting of his eyes, the little jerky nods of approval. He didn't talk to her and she wasn't expected to talk to him.

When his voice boomed out, she visibly jumped in shock. 'What?'

'I said, you've been a good girl, but you're going to sleep on me.'

'Sorry, I had a bad night.'

'Oh, why?' Harry draped a cloth over his work.

'Problems. They don't go away.'

'Don't run away from them!' Harry gave her a quick glance from his piercing blue eyes. 'I did.'

'Is there anything for me to see?' she asked.

'Not yet. You'll have to give me some more time.'

'I'd be proud to!' Renee stood up and stretched and Harry reacted to her graceful, unstudied pose with an artist's quick appreciation. 'Now you promised me you'd show me your exhibition pieces.'

'Katie likes them!' By contrast with his earlier mood, Harry looked happy and relaxed, his piercing, creative glance obviously juggling ideas in his mind. 'Listen, isn't that her old bomb?'

Renee laughed and walked to the open door of the studio. 'She really needs a new car. But an automatic this time—the clutch is nearly worn out.'

'Speaking of dreadful drivers,' Harry beetled his thick eyebrows, 'Ken Thomas owes a lot to you.'

'Nick, surely?' Renee looked back surprised.

'Nick mightn't have been quite so responsive if you hadn't wanted to help Ken. Mind you, he's got talent and Nick knows how to get the best out of everyone, but you played your part. Understand that very well.' Harry came to join Renee at the doorway and they both walked out into the sunshine as Katie swept into sight.

Over lunch, Harry and Katie talked long and enthusiastically about their work, his and hers, talk that was peppered with a few inevitable clashes, but highly satisfactory to both of them if the brightness of their eyes was anything to go by. Renee sat quietly and listened, while Harry gesticulated constantly and smote the air, and Katie forgot to eat so she could seize the moment to convey her opinion.

Looking lovingly at her aunt, Renee wondered if Harry knew just how much he depended on Katie. Apart from feeding the man properly several times a week, Katie was the highly qualified and articulate sounding board for all his ideas and it was obvious he respected her opinion, even if she had to fight him occasionally to voice it. All in all, they were a very attractive pair, and one day soon, something told Renee, Harry would put his past behind him and reach out for a new life. Katie had such a loving heart there was a whole avalanche awaiting the right man and there was no question in Katie's mind, Harry Caswell was the man her grandmother had promised her.

'Well, what a momentous day!' Katie said, on their way back to the farmhouse. 'Did you see how happy he was?'

Renee smiled at her. 'Things will sort themselves out in time.'

'What's that supposed to mean?' Katie went pink.

'I think the day is fast coming when Harry realises he can't do without you.'

'I told you, darling, he's not thinking of marriage.'

'Then make him think of it!' said Renee, very forcefully for her. 'You're not trying to take Beth's place, you're *you*. A new chapter in his life.'

'Oh—so he told you about Beth?'

'He said very little.' Renee shook her head, knowing she couldn't possibly undermine Katie's slight confidence. 'I remarked on the sculpture and he told me it was of his wife.'

Katie sighed. 'In heaven's name, how could I compete with that?'

'You're here, Katie,' Renee pointed out gravely, 'and you're a very special person.'

The dinner party at the Russells' was cancelled at the last moment because Cy had been called away unexpectedly to Brisbane. Renee took Sharon's phone call and they chatted amiably enough and arranged another date, but the next afternoon Philip called in at the farmhouse on his way home from work to invite Renee to the first night of a play the local repertory company was putting on.

'What is it?' Because he was looking so painfully eager, Renee smiled at him sweetly.

'Hedda Gabler.'

'Good grief, that's ambitious!'

'Yes, indeed. But really, they're not too bad. Hedda is the local schoolteacher, a quiet little thing until she gets on stage. Honestly, with make-up she can even look terrific. Do say you'll come?'

'I'd love to.' Again it wasn't strictly true, but Philip produced in her a sense of strained sympathy.

'I expect you'll enjoy it!' In his cream safari suit Philip looked very fresh and blond, a shy deprecating smile playing around his mouth. 'Of course we all know one another, so no one is too critical, but I think you'll find the standard acceptable. Actually acting is one of my outlets. I played the lead in our last play, *The Anniversary*. I committed suicide in the end.'

'Then perhaps it's just as well I didn't see it,' Renee smiled. 'Do you transform yourself as well?'

'I can think myself into a role.' Philip picked up his briefcase and moved to the front steps .'I'll call for you about seven—that will allow us plenty of time to park and be in our seats. Say hello to Katie for me.'

'I will.' Renee moved down the steps with him to his car. 'Thank you for asking me.'

'I was desperate for an excuse!' The hazel eyes that rested on her were full of intensity. 'Oh, by the way, they all dress up. You know, it makes an evening of it and the cast feel better.'

'I promise you won't be ashamed of me.'

'Oh, my!' For an instant he flicked her face and slender body, then he got into his car. 'See you, Renee!'

She smiled and stood back, watching until the car disappeared out of sight, then as Honey came up to nudge her with an old tennis ball in her mouth she bent down and tugged it out of the labrador's mouth as part of the game, then threw it in a shallow arc down towards the laden mango trees.

She had almost completed dressing when Katie called her to the phone.

'It's your mother, darling. You must speak to her.'

'I know.' Renee stood up from the dressing table and followed Katie out into the hallway, taking the receiver and sinking on to the carved chest at the same time. 'Hello, Mother.'

Katie went to move away, her face troubled, but Renee vigorously waved her back again, realising the futility of trying to interject. Her mother was already making it very plain that she was extremely annoyed with her daughter for her extraordinary behaviour and Renee could even feel the sheer bottled-up rage at the other end of the line.

'I warn you, I shall come up there!' Alicia cried over the wires.

'Please let me speak, Mother,' Renee cut in. 'The last thing I want to do is upset you and make you unhappy, but I've decided I can't possibly marry Simon. I don't love him.'

Whatever Alicia replied, Renee flushed scarlet and

she lifted her head to stare into Katie's eyes. 'Well, if he's there, I will speak to him.'

'Oh, darling!' Katie quavered, standing beside Renee with her hands clenched.

'Hello, Simon!' Renee said into the phone. She sat perfectly still as Simon spoke, but she was starting to go rather white. 'I shall stay here ... no, it's not a question of making up my mind. I don't love you, Simon ... you're making me feel utterly sick at heart. I don't care what Mother says ... *you've* been patient!' she gave an incredulous little laugh. 'May I remind you this is my aunt's home ... she is *not*!' Just as Katie went to jerk the phone from her niece, Renee gave a wild little laugh and crashed the phone down.

'What did he say, I want to know!' Katie said frenziedly.

'He says he's coming up.'

'Let him, but he won't stay here!'

'Don't upset yourself, Katie.' Renee could see the colour in her aunt's face and throat. 'It's a very sad thing, but I've never been able to communicate with my mother.'

'And I'll tell you why,' Katie said heatedly. 'Alicia has never listened to anybody. I shall write to her ... or better still, I'll fly down to Sydney.'

'You'll do no such thing!' Renee stood up and patted her aunt's shoulder. 'This is my fight, Katie, and I'm not going to be put down. I love my mother, but I'm not going to hand her over my life. I know I've allowed her to think I'll do anything she decides, but I'm not going to marry Simon. He means nothing to me, *nothing*, and I'm free of his jibes.'

'His jibes?' Katie questioned urgently. 'What could

he possibly say to you?'

'That I'm a statue that won't come to life among other things.' Not for the world would she have mentioned the brutal things.

'He must be mad!' Katie said harshly. 'He won't set foot on one inch of this farm. I'll get Nick to whip him off.'

'Please, Katie, don't let's tell Nick anything. I don't want him to think I'm a completely negligible person. I'll handle this in my own way. Besides, and this struck me as rather funny, he can't get away until the weekend. His father needs him more than I do.'

'Dear, dear, dear!' Katie stared sightlessly into the mirror.

'Forget it!' Renee turned her away. 'I haven't quite finished dressing. How do I look?'

'Lovely!' As she looked at her niece the two white lines faded from the sides of Katie's mouth. 'A blonde really shines in black and when it's chiffon and spotted in gold you'll get yourself into the paper.'

'Not too sophisticated? I brought the most ridiculous things.'

'Well,' Katie put her head to one side, 'I guess you're used to being stared at, but there will be people there all dressed up. You're sure to see Nick. And Sharon. Nick has to attend these things whether he likes it or not—it's all part of being a Garbutt and giving encouragement and example. Harry and I usually get along for some part of it.'

'Philip told me he played the lead in their last production.' Renee walked back to her bedroom and Katie followed her.

'Believe it or not, he was darned good. A rather

curious young man is Philip—a seething mass of repressions, yet he lets go on stage. I don't really want you to go out with him.'

'Heavens, Katie!' Renee whirled round in surprise.

'Don't show him too much kindness, darling,' Katie said seriously. 'He might see it as something else.'

'Oh, surely not!' Inside she was so stricken by the thought of seeing Nick again she couldn't take Philip seriously at all.

'I think he fancies himself in love with you already.'

Outside in the garden, Honey was barking, a sure indication that someone was coming, so Renee picked up her evening bag and walked towards her aunt. 'I promise you I won't say or do anything that could possibly be misconstrued.'

'Much the best way,' Katie smiled, 'but I don't think you realise your extraordinary attraction. Possibly it has something to do with your upbringing.'

'Gosh, don't talk about that!' Renee bent and kissed Katie's cheek. 'We'll leave the question of Mother and Simon. I want to enjoy myself tonight.'

When she opened the front door to Philip, his hazel eyes positively embraced her, sweeping from her shining hair to her black and gold sandals. 'You look beautiful!'

It was a phrase she had heard often, but never more fervently.

'Thank you.'

'How are you, Katie?' He gave Katie a quick smiling glance.

'Fine, dear. You two go off and enjoy yourselves. I'll have supper waiting.'

Just for a second Philip looked flustered. 'Thanks a

lot, Katie, but I've booked a table at Carlo's.'

'Well then, I'll just ask you not to be too late. Renee has to be over at Harry's in the morning—he's working on a cast of her head. I expect she'll tell you about it.'

In the car, Renee hid her amused smile. It wasn't like Katie to come on as 'Aunty', so she must have recognised in Philip something Renee barely saw. They made small talk all the way into town, Philip telling her all about their amateur theatricals, and his past successes, so there was really no need for Renee to commit herself in any way. Talking about the things he liked, Philip seemed a changed person and not the somewhat embittered young man she had met at her party.

They had no difficulty finding themselves a parking spot reasonably close to the old picture theatre that was now used for other purposes and only when they were settled in their seats did Philip mention carelessly:

'Nick lets us use it, though he stills owns the property. Garbutt money opened up this town and brought in the settlers. I think you're perfectly well aware he still owns most of it.'

'From what I've seen and heard, he's very generous with his time and his money.' Renee rotated in her seat a little to look around the hall. The walls appeared freshly painted in a pale green picked out with gold and the emerald green curtain looked rather sumptuous. Even the chairs were comfortable, though a few of them had a joyful squeak. Fifteen minutes before the curtain was due to go up, the hall was more than half filled, and the next five minutes saw a fresh influx and Nick's arrival with Sharon, in sunshine yellow, clinging to his arm, her dark excited eyes searching the stalls and fixing on Renee and Philip with great accuracy.

She gave a little wave and Renee waved back, so jolted inside it was like a tremendous assault. How could she endure to be around when Nick took Sharon for his wife? Only gradually did she become aware Philip was staring at her.

'What's the matter?' he asked.

'In what way?' At least she had found her voice.

'You went sort of funny. Far away.'

'I was thinking. I had a phone call from home before I came out.'

'Not bad news, I hope?' Philip's head moved closer to her in concern.

'Oh, no!' They had to draw in their feet as a couple shuffled by smilingly.

In the dimmed golden light she saw Nick and Sharon take their places a few rows ahead and all of a sudden, everything seemed oppressive, the air and the crowd. It was all she could do not to jump up and run out. After that first minute, Nick hadn't even glanced their way and it upset her out of all proportion, making her feel desolate and abandoned. If only she had never met him, for she would never forget him.

The curtain went up and the play opened. Tesman and Hedda, his wife, have returned from their honeymoon the preceding night. Miss Tesman, the aunt with whom he had lived, arrives early in the morning to see if everything is all right.

'Why, what a gorgeous bonnet you've been investing in!'

So good was the set, the costumes and the acting, Renee began to breathe again. It wasn't the first time she had seen the play, but the local schoolteacher was astonishingly good, playing the iron-willed, unrelenting Hedda for all she was worth.

At the end of the first act there was a little silence before the applause broke out. Philip glanced at Renee sideways, a curious mixture of appeal and apprehension in his eyes. 'Something's upsetting you, isn't it?'

'In a sense, I suppose it's the play!' She looked up from the programme in her lap. 'She's very good, your Miss Grayson.'

'Yes, I feel she's wasting herself in amateur theatricals. Tesman's performance isn't so sound, do you think?'

Renee rattled off something, trying to keep her eyes from straying to Nick's dark profile. She minded unbearably seeing Sharon with Nick. Indeed, had she known, she wouldn't have made this arrangement with Philip. He was eyeing her so curiously it was a relief when the curtain went up again, the strength of her own emotions increasing the drama.

By the end of the evening, and Hedda's really gripping suicide, she was positively wrung out. Yet she clapped, along with everyone else until her palms were quite pink.

'Come backstage and we'll meet the cast,' Philip urged, grasping her arm and guiding her through the throng.

He gave her no chance to resist him even if she were capable of it and of course when they arrived in the wings Nick was kissing Hedda's cheek, saying something to her that made her smile brilliantly.

Renee couldn't back away. She could do nothing but go forward and make Philip happy by meeting and congratulating his friends. Seen close to and under a truly professional make-up, Thea Grayson who had played Hedda was really a plain girl and it gave Renee a start, for she had looked almost beautiful on stage, moving and acting with a beautiful woman's confidence. But good actress though she was, she couldn't hide her interest in Philip, her large blue eyes, her best feature, shifting constantly back and forth to his face.

'You're coming on to the party, aren't you?' she stood beside Philip, glancing uncertainly at Renee. 'Do say you're coming. You too, Miss Dalton, of course.'

'I'm sorry,' Renee trailed away a little, finding herself incapable of acting festive when she felt like weeping, 'it's very kind of you to ask me, but I have an early appointment in the morning.'

'Oh, well!' Thea tried to pull herself together. 'Perhaps you can run Miss Dalton home and come on?' Her blue eyes fixed themselves on Philip's face.

'Not tonight!' Philip's finality of tone was scarcely polite and hearing him, Sharon swung around, sparkling and vivacious in her off the shoulder dress.

'Oh, *do* come, even if it's only for supper. You said you would, Pip!'

'Sorry, Renee's got a headache.'

If she hadn't one before she had it now, for Nick turned around to join them, the light highlighting his bronze skin and his high cheekbones, the startling, heavily lashed silver-grey eyes.

'Hi!' His glance just skimmed Renee's face. 'Don't tell me the play unsettled you?'

'I enjoyed it as much as everyone else did!' She tried to smile politely, aware of some faint hostility in him.

'Hello, Philip,' he greeted the younger man coolly, very tall and dark and somehow a little hard and formidable.

'Good evening, Nick.' Philip coloured faintly. 'Going along to the party?'

'Aren't we all?' He glanced back at Renee with a disconcerting suddenness. 'I think you'll enjoy it.'

'Yes, come on, don't be a spoilsport!' There was something a little challenging to Sharon's charming smile.

'It's just that I wasn't expecting it,' Renee said, and smiled at Thea apologetically. 'If you want me, I'd love to come for a little while.'

'Oh great!' Thea brightened visibly. 'I'll go and take my make-up off.'

A light was showing in Katie's room when she finally arrived back at the farmhouse. They had stayed on for more than an hour and it had seemed like a year, with Nick so cool and snappy she could have slapped him or burst into tears. When he had asked her to dance with him she had, at first, declined, but he had pulled her to her feet as though he would have liked to slap her himself, telling her flatly, as Katie had done, not to get entangled with Philip, even out of kindness.

It wasn't kindness Philip wanted from her, as he had proved in the car, clasping her head with both hands and kissing her mouth before he let her out. *Forgive me, I couldn't help myself!*

She had wanted to tell him it wasn't any use, but he started the car up immediately, calling to her that he would ring her.

'You're late,' Katie said, catching the bridge of her reading glasses and shoving them back up her nose.

'There was a party afterwards.'

'I should have guessed.' Katie patted the side of the bed. 'You don't look happy.'

'I can't pretend with you, Katie. Incidentally, you were right about Philip. I think he finds me attractive.'

'He takes himself too seriously, that young man.'

'Nick was there.' Renee pulled her earrings off as if they were hurting her. 'And Sharon.'

'Naturally!' Katie punched the pillow. 'I guess you've fallen in love with him.'

'It would be hard not to. Except that, tonight, he acted as if he didn't even like me.'

'How's that?' Katie pulled her glasses off and put them away in their case.

'Like you, he warned me about Philip. Is there something about that young man I don't know?'

'After his mother died, he had some kind of nervous collapse. There might have been more. I know Cy was very worried about him and Nick put him into a good job to get him on his feet. Not that their efforts have been wasted, he's improved a good deal, but I don't think you could call Philip a strong character. The way he talks about his father, one might expect some kind of tyrant, but Cy's a good man and he's done his best for his children,' Katie assured her.

'I can't help feeling sorry for him,' Renee said, and promptly yawned. 'The girl who played Hedda is in love with him, I'm sure.'

'Thea?' Katie picked up a glass of water, sipped it,

and put it back on the bedside table. 'You astonish me.'

'She looks at him with her heart in her eyes, as the saying goes!' Renee swept off the bed, leaned forward and kissed Katie's forehead. 'I'm going to bed. By rights, I should have had an early night. Nick and I don't exactly clash, but there was a certain arrogance on him tonight.'

'Maybe he was really concerned about your effect on Philip. Surely you've seen the boy gazing at you?'

'Not really.' Inside Renee held herself very quiet. The perfect image of Nick was clearly in her mind, but she couldn't recall Philip's adoring glance, from a total lack of interest. 'Do you believe in love at first sight, Katie?' she asked dreamily.

'Some are lucky to have that dream materialise,' Katie laughed gently. 'Are you telling me you fell in love with Nick at first sight?'

'Actually he frightened me,' Renee confessed.

'But you're past that?' Katie's blue eyes were shrewd.

'There's no way it could turn out well, Katie,' Renee said sadly, curving her face away from her aunt's intent glance. 'But good or bad, I'll never forget him.'

'Why don't you stay with me all summer?' Katie suggested.

'I couldn't darling, not if there's something between Sharon and Nick.' Renee stood in the doorway, the light gleaming in her hair and the gold spots on her dress. She looked very fragile, almost ethereal, her delicate face alive with her feelings.'

'They're not engaged,' Katie pressed. 'Why aren't they? Sharon still has the bloom of a peach, but she's not getting any younger.'

'She loves him.' Renee shook her head.

'Perhaps. Hero-worship isn't love and there's a time it has to end.'

'Anyway, there's no way I could dazzle him,' Renee announced abruptly. 'Shall I turn out your light?'

'Thank you, darling,' Katie smiled. 'I'll get breakfast in the morning. You have a sleep in.'

'At least Nick was generous enough to say I could take out Star Dust any time I liked.'

Isn't he being nice to you!' Katie's voice was smooth and bland. 'Parties, horses, even a car.'

'He's only being polite. Goodnight, Katie.'

'Pleasant dreams, darling,' Katie called, and Renee could hear the note of warm teasing.

The next morning she drove over to Harry's for her next sitting and on the way back to the farmhouse she passed Ken Thomas travelling the other way in his noisy little car.

'Pull over!'

She could feel the laughter bubbling in her as he mouthed and gesticulated wildly, so she brought the car Nick had lent her to a standstill on the wide grassy strip bordering a small dairy farm. In the rear vision she saw Ken doing a U-turn, then the next moment he passed her to pull up a few feet ahead.

'Hi, friend!' Ken was out of his car and walking towards her, so Renee swung out as well, shaking her long hair back from her face.

'How are you, Ken?'

'Working like a slave!'

'Great!' Her voice was warm and encouraging.

'I want to please everyone.' Ken's eyes were blazing. 'You, Nick, dear little Sharon who's been as sweet as poison!' Neighbours passed in their cars, and Ken lifted a hand and waved, his gaze returning to Renee's face. 'Believe it or not, sweetie, she's very jealous of you.'

'Me?' Renee could feel the blood burn in her face. 'Why?'

'You ought to know!' Ken mocked her. 'This was a little present from Nick, wasn't it?' He drew a hand over the yellow bonnet of the Sunbird.

'Only for as long as I'm here,' she murmured. 'You must allow he's a very generous man.'

'Granted, but you still have your own effect on him, for which I for one am extremely grateful. And how is Harry?'

'Working very well.'

'I'm glad to hear that.' Ken drew back a little to stare down at her flushed face. 'I wonder if you know you're a catalyst?'

'Meaning I seem to be stirring things up around here?'

'In more ways than one!' Ken shrugged. 'Sharon even made a point of asking whether *I* could ever fall in love with you.'

'To which you said?' Her luminous eyes flashed a deeper green.

'Easily!' he answered lightheartedly. 'You know, she even sounded jealous.'

'So don't go bothering to use me to provoke a crisis,' she warned him. 'For one thing, I'm going home shortly.'

'Whatever for?' He drew back dismayed. 'You've only just got here.'

'And I'm loving it, but I have my life to arrange.'

'This guy you're engaged to?'

'I'm *not* engaged!' Renee breathed unequivocally. 'Who told you that?'

'Sharon.' Ken narrowed his eyes against the brilliant sunshine. 'I'm quite sure she said you were engaged, or almost.'

'No.' Renee shook her head. 'Perhaps Sharon doesn't trust her own feeling for you.'

'If I could only believe that!' Ken drew in his breath sharply, a bitter smile about his mouth. 'It's just that she has this insane notion Nick is going to ask her to marry him. Surely if he was going to, he'd have done it by now?'

'Who knows about Nick!' Renee sighed.

'Don't tell me you're a damned fool about him too?' Ken asked in a shocked tone.

'He's a very romantic figure!' Renee forced the mocking reply when inside she was cursing herself for that betraying little sigh. 'Does everyone have to be in love with him?'

'*My* girl, anyway!' Ken glanced down and kicked a stone. 'What about coming swimming with me to-morrow? We'll go up to the lake. I've been working so hard I can afford to take a short break.'

'Sorry, Ken, I'll be busy,' Renee made her excuses. 'My mother is coming up this weekend.'

'Not trouble?' Ken asked with some concern.

'Just something to thrash out,' Renee answered evasively, then lifted her hand to shade her eyes. 'We seem to be in a very public spot. Surely that's Sharon's car?'

'Hell!' Ken couldn't help his explosive retort. He

swung around quickly, just as Sharon chose to pull up directly opposite them, thrusting her dark head through the open window and calling rather sarcastically:

'What is this? Some new romantic assignation?'

'Take it for granted, dear!' Ken returned waspishly. 'Tell us some more gossip.'

'Hello, Sharon!' Renee said in her soft, polite style.

'Hi!' Sharon's black eyes were flashing brilliantly. 'I'm sure *you* didn't suggest meeting here?'

'You don't object?' Renee couldn't help herself.

'Hardly. I've got the man I want.'

'Meaning Nick?' Ken lifted his eyebrows superciliously. 'That's putting it a bit strongly, my girl. We see no diamond, no emerald.'

'I'd better be going,' Renee said hastily. 'Katie is expecting me back for lunch.'

At this Sharon appeared to relax to the extent that she got out of her car and crossed the road. 'I'm so glad you enjoyed the play last night.'

'I did!' Renee's green glance was very clear and direct. 'Hedda was marvellous.'

'You mean I missed something?' Ken enquired. 'Anyway, I was working until three this morning.'

'Such a change!' Sharon smiled brilliantly into his tense, bearded face. 'Next you'll be telling us you're going to abandon your irresponsible bachelor's life?'

'I *did* want to marry you!' he muttered.

'Poor creature!'

Renee, who wasn't enjoying this exchange, opened the door of the Sunbird. 'You don't mind if I take myself off?'

'Before you go,' Sharon looked in at her, smiling gaily, 'I want to tell you how much Philip enjoyed your company last night. I had to listen to him all through breakfast.'

'Why didn't you get up and go out?' Ken challenged her. 'Renee's hardly aware of your brother's existence.'

'That's not the way *I* heard it!' Sharon smiled.

'Philip's trouble is, he puts his own construction on everything,' Ken answered for Renee rather wearily. 'Renee would be too nice to put him in his place.'

'How insensitive you are!' Sharon jumped back as if she wanted to strike him. 'You've never liked Philip.'

'Don't be a goat!' he grabbed at her hand. 'I don't dislike him, I just think he's weak.'

'*He's* weak!'

Renee switched on the ignition and reversed clear of them. 'I'll leave you both to talk this over. So long!'

Sharon wasn't so upset she couldn't pull herself together enough to wave and when Renee looked into her rear vision, she saw Ken taking Sharon by the shoulders, pulling her into his car. A minute later she lost sight of them as she turned a corner, but the vision remained. Despite her indignation, Sharon hadn't been pulling away.

Katie had lunch waiting for her and they talked over the events of the morning and the return of Harry's wonderful enthusiasm until it was time for Katie to return to her work. They had already established a routine and while Katie was working Renee had decided on taking Star Dust out for a ride. So many feelings of trepidation were building up in her they demanded release, and the fact that Philip had talked about her incessantly came as a jarring shock. It wasn't right that he had kissed her, but she could hardly have avoided it, the way his thin hands had grasped her face to press an unwanted, unsolicited kiss on her mouth. It wasn't unpleasant. Like everything Philip appeared to do, it simply didn't rate.

One of the aboriginal boys saddled up the mare for her and as she left the stables complex she became aware that a blue cattle dog was following her, apparently bent on going for a run.

'Home, boy!' she called out as the dog caught up to her, its tongue lolling in a huge smile. 'Go on, go home!'

The big bluey ignored her, as though nothing could be further from its mind. It was used to following the horses, and it would stick along for a mile or two. Renee wasn't really worried. The mare didn't resent the dog's company, in fact its presence was adding to the enjoyment of the ride.

'What's your name?' Renee called, something that was typical of her because she thought it entirely natural to talk to animals.

The dog simply grinned again, had a good roll, then caught up, gaining Renee's respect for its stamina. This was a working dog, but it was young and it still liked to play. When the distant shimmer of a lagoon enticed her, the dog began to bark.

'What is it, boy?'

Renee reined the mare in and looked down to the dark green line of the trees. The grass was growing thicker, taller, and electric blue flowers wreathed the long shoots. They were about an hour's ride from the homestead and this was the first time the dog had barked. A commotion of birds exploded overhead and immediately the cattle dog chased them, not slacking until the birds reached the next belt of trees where they settled in a raucous sympathy.

For a few seconds Renee hesitated, then she rode off in the direction of the water. The scenery was entrancing, a virgin wilderness, and she gazed at it steadfastly, as if impressing it on her memory for life. Emerald was in every way a study in immensity; the infinite blue sky and the measureless land ocean. Some could even find it overpowering, the vast, limitless space with no other sound but the sound of the wind and the song of the birds, but she was conscious of a tremendous feeling of physical and spiritual kinship.

But life in the wilds could never be without incident. As the mare scented the cool freshness of the paperbark-shaded lagoon, she picked up her stride, carrying Renee swiftly on her journey to the water. In the distance the cattle dog started up its barking, a sound that was vaguely plaguing Renee because it seemed like a warning, and just as she turned her head, the sure-footed mare stumbled over something lying concealed in the grass, propped badly and threw its rider over its head.

When Renee opened her eyes—it might have been only a few seconds—she sat up in pain and bewilderment, exploring her aching head with groping fingers, crying out in sudden horror as she realised something was watching her from the long grass. For an instant panic froze her limbs, then she recovered so fast she was on her feet, taking the same flight path as the bolting mare. She didn't know what to expect of the black feral boar, but she knew better than to stay. Wild pigs were unpredictable and they had been known to charge riders on horseback.

Just ahead of her the cattle dog was making dancing leaps through the long grass, barking ferociously at something behind her, and when she turned in terror, the boar was charging, making her pulses jump in shock. If she could only outrun it to the trees! Adrenalin was tingling through her body, the thrill of fear. She thought fleetingly of the mare, but it had disappeared across the savannah. It was painful now, running, shivering yet sweat stained, and as she vaulted over fallen branches and the roots of tangled vines, a strong hook snatched at her flying feet and brought her down.

She fell heavily, the blood beating in her ears, and above the mad thud of her heart, the cattle dog's barking. As she flipped her body over, she almost fainted with pain, so severe she didn't have the breath to cry out. It was her ankle, and she gave a stifled gasp, watching with dread as the boar and the cattle dog closed on one another. She could only think the cattle dog was protecting her, for it had placed itself squarely in the boar's path, taking a stand, and making so much noise the pig propped and rooted at the ground.

It seemed to be trying to decide whether to attack, but in a few moments it raced forward, slashing at the cattle dog with its vicious tusks. Renee had a kaleidoscope impression of dust and grass and blood and lunging animal bodies. Her nails were raked into the ground and she tried to slither backwards, certain the boar would kill the gallant dog. If there were only some way she could help it. She was nearly fainting with pain and her head was swimming so badly she couldn't think.

There was a stout stick behind her, if she could only reach it. Then what would she do? Throw it. She felt so weak. Both animals were locked in a death struggle and she felt ill and spinning, absolutely helpless. Tears were running down her paper-white face and she didn't even glimpse the party of riders that broke out of the trees with exquisite timing, riding directly for her and the bloody, enraged animals.

A shot rang out, then another, and she lay back on the ground, trembling and sobbing soundlessly, until Nick himself was beside her. His face was so set it might have been cast in bronze, his eyes beneath the wide brim of his hat so brilliant they had the flash of lightning.

'It's all right, Renee. It's all right!' He laid the rifle down carefully and turned his attention to her aching body.

At the first gentle probing touch of his hands, the burning knot of pain miraculously eased. 'It's my ankle,' she collected herself sufficiently to whisper. 'The left one.'

'God!' his breath came in a harsh exclamation.

'The mare stumbled....'

'Hush, don't talk. We knew something was wrong when it galloped into camp. Give me that knife, Tom.' He held out his hand to one of his men.

'What happened to the bluey?' Renee gasped. 'It seemed to be protecting me.'

'It was.' His brilliant glance sharpened over her. 'I'll have to get this boot off, Renee. Then I'll take you home. Geoff,' he lifted his head to speak to one of the anxious faces bending over her, 'ride ahead and get Doc Stevens. I want him at the house as soon as possible. Tell him what's happened. Kelly, circle back and bring up the jeep.'

'You haven't told me about the bluey!' Renee was so

white her skin was the colour of alabaster.

'It's all right!' Nick answered, pressing her back into the ground.

'It's all my fault!' A stifled sob broke from her. 'You're not telling me the truth; are you?'

'Lie quietly!' His eyes blazed in his dark face. 'I'll try to be as gentle as possible.'

Vaguely Renee heard the command, but by the time she was free of her riding boot, she had slumped into unconsciousness.

The journey back to the homestead was hazy, and the doctor arrived less than ten minutes after Nick carried her into the house. She had suffered a light concussion, no more, bruising and a badly sprained ankle.

'You were lucky, my dear!' The doctor raised his heavy, silvered eyebrows. 'Maybe you know this already?'

'Yes.' She lay back quietly, her green eyes on the kindly, disciplined face. 'No one will tell me about the cattle dog. What happened?'

'It couldn't be saved, my dear,' the doctor patted her hand, 'but it did exactly what it intended to do— protected you.'

'I'll never forget that!' Her eyes filled with tears and she turned her head aside. 'It was so happy running beside the mare. And to think its life is over!'

'It couldn't let the boar harm you,' Doctor Stevens told her finally. 'I once had an old labrador who pulled me right over before she let me tread on a snake. I have a great respect for dogs, for their intelligence and devotion. Horses are superb, but they don't love you like a dog does.'

'I think it even knew there was danger.'

'Maybe.' The blue eyes were keen. 'It probably remembered the last shoot. We don't have the big problem of the grain growers of the Central downs, but now and again Nick has to organise a shoot. Feral pigs can be quite savage and they attack without provocation.'

'I know.'

'Well, that's it, young lady!' The doctor stood up, tall and spare. 'Bed rest for you and there'll be no problem. Alternate hot and cold compresses for the ankle. I'll leave some pain-killers for you to get through the night.'

Renee thanked him and lay back, the tears glittering behind her closed eyes. She was terribly upset by the death of the dog. She would remember the incident for a long time and the total pleasure she had felt before the disastrous attack. She should never have gone riding through the long grass, but at least the mare was safe.

'Renee?'

Nick had come back into the bedroom, gazing down at her.

'I'm sorry, Nick.' Her colour had brightened a little, and her hair rippled across the pillow like gilt.

'Why in God's name did you ride that way?' he demanded.

'Because I'm an absolute fool!' she answered him with painful difficulty. 'I know you told me to keep to the river, but I simply didn't think of any danger. I'm a city girl and it shows.'

'You gave me the worst moments of my life,' he said quietly, then went to the French doors that led on

to the verandah and drew the insect screen. 'I thought
you had sense.'

'*Please*, Nick!' The tears slid out of her eyes and on
to the pillow.

His nostrils flared and he lifted one hand and let it
drop. 'I think you ought to get out of your riding
things.'

'What shall I wear?'

'Oh, something. One of my robes. Katie will bring
your things. I've sent a man over to wait for her.
She's not at home.'

'Then she must be at Harry's.' Renee looked confused. 'She was working when I left and she didn't say
anything about going anywhere.'

'She's not at Harry's either. Maybe she took a quick
trip into town. Anyway, Katie's not the problem.'

'I don't have to stay here, Nick,' she said, with a catch
in her voice.

'I'm not letting you out of my sight. I can't help it.'
He stood without moving, staring over her head at a
painting on the wall. 'It's partly my fault. I should
never have let you go out on your own.'

'So you won't forgive me for the loss of a good working dog?' She was shaking with despair, not liking
his curious stillness and the remoteness of his eyes. 'I'm
sorry, Nick. More sorry than I can say.'

'However it was,' he lowered his gaze to stare at her,
'all my fears were for you. When the mare bolted into
camp I was prepared to find you with your neck
broken.' His black brows were drawn together and his
eyes glittered, but he spoke entirely without emotion.
'Now I want to be sure you're perfectly all right, so
you don't go home.'

He looked as proud as Lucifer and extremely hard, and Renee's heart gave a great lunge of pain and fright. 'I'll wait until Katie comes to change.'

'No, I'll help. You'll find me very competent.'

There was a tear-bright glitter in Renee's brilliant green eyes. 'Why are you being so cruel to me?'

'Cruel—*God*!' his mouth twisted in a controlled anger. 'You've had a bad time of it, Renee, but so have I. Now, let me find you something to wear. This is my mother's room.'

She was incapable of comment, watching him walk away to the mirrored door of a walk-in wardrobe. Being the sort of man he was, he was quite capable of following up his plan to get her out of her ruined jeans and stained shirt. The large room around her was gentle and feminine in a blue and white colour scheme, accented with touches of a deeper turquoise. At another time she would have loved the refined luxury, now she was a shaking bundle of nerves.

'Will this do?' Nick came back towards her, clasping a silk robe in a deep ruby shade.

'Thank you.' It was magnificent really, embroidered around the cuffs and the pockets and the softly rolled lapels with gold scrolls. 'Go away, Nick,' she begged him, even as she wanted him to stay. He was so vital it was sufficient to draw a little strength from him.

'What for?' His eyes probed the slender contours of her body. 'Do you think I'd be scandalised by the sight of a woman's body?'

'I can't fight you!' She spoke emotionally, dizzy and trembling as she tried to sit up.

'Then don't try!' His expression softened miraculously as he came to her side, holding her with exquisite gentleness as she moved her legs gingerly over the side of the bed.

'What's happening to me? I haven't any strength.' She was leaning against his arm, the quick tears springing to her eyes.

'In the first place,' he said tersely, 'you're still in shock and you must be aching all over. Let me help you, little one. I swear I won't hurt you any more than I can help. Then you can curl up and go to sleep.'

'No.'

'You will. That injection will start working.'

She tried to fumble with the buttons of her shirt, but her head was swimming.

'Let me.'

She closed her eyes and after a moment he eased her shirt off. She crossed her arms across her breasts while he released the catch on her bra, then it fell to the ivory carpet as she slipped her arms into the cool silk of the robe.

'Lie down, little one.'

At the sound of his impassive tone she flicked her eyes open. 'I've hacked so much at your jeans they should come off fairly easily.'

Weakly now she watched his grave face, crying out as the leg of her jeans came off her damaged ankle.

'I'm sorry. God, I'm sorry!' His voice came low and compassionate. 'Relax, baby, it's all over.'

The slanting rays of the sun shone across the room, shining dully on her gilt hair and the ruby robe. She looked extremely fragile and he bent and readjusted the pillows under her head. 'Would you like something over you?'

'No.' She was lying on top of the bedclothes, but the robe was enough for her.

'Don't think about anything, Renee. Just sleep.'

She didn't answer but opened her eyes, shining against the satin smoothness of her white skin. 'You won't tell anybody you helped me undress?'

'Would it worry you?'

'Everything about you worries me. It's so difficult not to do what you tell me.'

'Then close your eyes,' he said. 'When you wake up, Katie will be here.'

When Katie did arrive, exclaiming and white-faced with anxiety, Renee was deep in a drugged sleep. A soft light was in the room and it bloomed over her relaxed body and her delicate young face.

'Oh, Nick!' Katie wailed very softly.

'She's perfectly all right!' With a quick gesture Nick put his arm around her and pulled her against him. 'I wouldn't have had it happen for the world, but it did, and she's come out of it miraculously well.'

'What did Doctor Stevens say?'

'What I'm telling you. All she has to do is keep off that ankle.'

'I just love her so much....'

'I know.' Gently he took one of Katie's shaking hands and kissed it. 'What you need is a stiff drink. For that matter, so do I!'

CHAPTER SIX

WHEN Renee opened her eyes again, she couldn't even recall where she was, yet the first word she uttered was a name.

'Nick!'

'I'm here.' He came to stand at the bedside, fixing his eyes on her puzzled face. 'How do you feel?'

'Confused.' She brushed her hand across her eyes, the gold embroidery on the robe glinting in the soft light.

'You've slept for almost ten hours. It's three o'clock in the morning.'

'Haven't you been asleep at all?' She took her arm away, staring up at him as though fascinated.

'But of course,' he lied. 'I just wanted to be near you when you woke up. You're on Emerald.'

'I know!' Her voice trailed away and she gazed around the room. 'Where's Katie?'

'She's been here and she went home again. In the confusion she left Honey locked in the house. She knows you're being well looked after and I'll take you home later on this morning.'

'Poor Katie!' Unbidden, all Renee's pulses were stirring, and she wanted Nick to gather her up in his arms and comfort her. No, not *comfort*. She knew that perfectly well, the tips of her breasts taut against the silk robe. 'May I have a drink of water?'

'You can have anything you like,' he told her. 'It's

enough for me to see you looking so much better.'

'My headache is gone.' Her green eyes were fixed on a point between his wide shoulders. He was still wearing the clothes she had last seen him in and she knew now he had had no sleep at all. 'You're being awfully good to me, Nick.'

Gently he lifted her, supporting her while she drank. 'That makes quite a change from cruel.'

'I never dreamed I could let anyone. . . .'

'Be at peace, little one.' He put her down on the pillows again. I'm the soul of chivalry.'

'And yet. . . .' With a sigh she put up her arm.

'Katie trusts me,' he murmured, his hand warm as it joined with her own.

'So do I.'

'*You're* the one who shouldn't!' He released her, a wry smile curving the beautifully delineated mouth. 'Do you thing you can go back to sleep again?'

'No.'

'You sound very definite.'

'I'm not even sure this isn't all taking place in a dream.' She let her eyes move over his face, while her blood kept singing and urging. 'I've never had a man in my bedroom before.'

'Never?'

The tone was silky and she opened her green eyes wide. 'Occasionally Father used to come in and say goodnight to me when I was a child.'

'He was a very lucky man to have had such a beautiful little daughter.'

'I think he just took that for granted. You haven't seen my mother.'

'You didn't enjoy your childhood very much, did

you?' Nick sat down in the armchair again, so she had to look across at him. Flamboyantly male, eyes faintly mocking.

'Why did you move away from me?' she asked.

'I thought it was a good idea,' he said softly. 'You're the one so certain of the dauntless strength of my will.'

'If only Sharon were here with us.'

'I've no answer to that.' There was an amused little break in his vibrant voice. 'Go to sleep, little one. You might as well.'

'My ankle's hurting.' And it was, but it scarcely seemed to matter.

'So? I suppose we can bathe it.'

'I don't want to move.' In the soft light, her green eyes looked huge and excited, her long silky hair falling in a gilt stream over the ruby silk. 'Do you think I can have another drink of water? I seem to be very thirsty.'

'It won't work,' he warned her, and got up to pour a glass of water.

'What won't?' she asked, and immediately flushed. 'It seems very funny you're cautioning me. I'm not trying to lure you to my bed.'

'That's fine. I'm at my lowest ebb right now.' His silver eyes sparkled over her, then he came to the bed, half lifting her as he pushed the pillows to her back.

'That's odd,' she told him tautly. 'The first thing I noticed about you was your dynamic strength.'

'It's disintegrating!'

She almost snatched the glass away from him, humiliated by his sharp humour. 'Thank you!'

'You're very welcome, my lady.' He watched her while she drank, then he took the glass away and set it down on the bedside table. 'Perhaps if I kissed you goodnight, you'd relax?'

'I'm sure those aren't the doctor's orders!' she said tartly.

'Why are you angry?'

His question caught her off guard. She *was* angry. Angry with him. Angry with herself for so foolishly trying to provoke him—no, seduce him. It was shocking and so lamentably out of character. Was it possible she had a dual nature, or had her real nature caught up with her?

'You can leave now!' With her last strength she gave the imperious little order, half turning her body away from him.

Nick gave an appreciative laugh as though she had made a little joke. 'You need a smack for that.' There was a change in his voice. A male dominance.

Renee was agonisingly aware of him standing over her, then in the next instant he sank on to the bed behind her, drawing her back into his arms. 'Where would you like this chaste salute, on the forehead, or the cheek, or the nose?'

'Anywhere. Everywhere.' She reacted frantically to the hard mockery.

'So I'll do what you tell me.' His eyes moved slowly from her face to the tender swell of her breasts, consuming her so she had to shut her eyes against a tumultuous rush of passion.

'I'll go to sleep, Nick, truly I will.' Even her voice shook.

'You should have been so accommodating when you had the chance!' He lifted her still higher into his arms. 'Come here, Renee. Closer.'

The sensuality in his voice was overlaid by a devastating tenderness, a terrible persuasion, that made her give a little inarticulate moan. Her eyes closed and she parted her lips in anticipation of his, flooded by the exquisite memory of when he had made love to her before. Tomorrow she could be strong, but now she hungered too much.

His hand was on her throat, such a strong, finely sculpted hand, tilting her head back still further. The hard strength of his body, the warmth and the closeness was so thrilling, she had the curious feeling she was going off into space ... floating ... melting ... outside of her body. She had never wanted anything so badly as the touch of his mouth, yet when it came, exploring her own, deeper and deeper, it wasn't enough.

He held her so closely she could feel the blood pounding in her veins. Her heart was a wild thing dashing itself against her rib cage. Tumultuous feelings were storming in her, a demand that shook her. If he stopped now she would die, yet there had to be an end to this torment.

'Nick?' Her voice was anguished against his mouth. 'I want you to love me. *Please*. This is unbearable!'

'Isn't it!' He didn't contradict her. 'Crazy!'

She might have murmured his name again, taking his hand and lowering it to her breast, taut with yearning, moaning a little for the shattering pleasure it gave her.

'*God!*'

She heard the swift intake of his breath as if a whip flicked him, a shocked moment when he seemed to draw back, then both his hands claimed the satin contours of her breasts.

The silk robe slipped to her waist, a pool of flame, while she clung to him in ecstasy, her skin full of light, very white against the red silk, her hair a glittering mantle cascading over her shoulders. She had waited so long to feel like this, to know herself a woman. Now she could wait no longer.

'You make me feel beautiful!' Her soft voice sounded like music.

'You are.'

She closed her eyes as his mouth touched her breast.

'I love you.' She said it very softly at first, then over and over, so a great tension tore through him and he held her away from him, grasping her two hands and holding them tight.

'Listen to me, Renee. *Listen.*' He spoke harshly, with a great effort. 'Love is a pretty strong word. It should mean something, something powerful and binding. I'm not going to let you use it too lightly.'

'But I do!' She was so shocked, so saddened, she couldn't lift her head from the pillow. 'I can't imagine life without you. That's obvious, isn't it? I could never let anyone touch me but you. Doesn't it impress you, all the power you have over me? It *should!*'

Almost abstractedly he pulled the robe over her white body. 'In a little while it will be morning.'

'And we can pretend this didn't happen.' Her eyes filled with tears.

'Don't sound so heartbroken!' Very gently Nick kissed her mouth. 'What about all the problems you have to solve? *I'm* not going to solve them for you— you've got to do it on your own. If you're supposed to be a real woman, you'd better finish with this Simon. Isn't he coming up here?'

'Who cares!' She blinked away the glittering tears.

'You let it happen.' He held her chin so she had to look at him.

'I told him not to come.'

'Evidently he doesn't attach much importance to what you say.'

'That's my own fault,' she admitted sadly. 'Everything is my fault.'

'Then break out of your sheltered world. I'm not going to concern myself.'

'Why should you?' She looked at him, a desperate expression on her lovely face. 'Let them come. Let them *all* come. I really love you, Nick, you know that. I'm sorry if it's an embarrassment. I never meant it to happen.'

'You *suppose* you love me,' he returned a little cruelly. 'How do you know it isn't I excite you?'

'Oh, stop it!' she pleaded. 'How can I fathom such deep feeling? I didn't even know I was a sensual person. It's all such a shock. Don't make me hate myself!'

'Nothing like that,' he said decisively. 'If you know yourself a little better, I'm glad. But you have to work out your own life.'

'I suppose I must.'

'You must!'

He rose quickly, looking so hard and determined she could only stare at him. Her mind flashed back to the moment she had met him. He was no different then. Only she had changed.

Asserting herself proved as difficult as she imagined, for her mother arrived with Simon, sweeping up the same emotional storms. Renee was even glad she had her bound ankle as an excuse to lie back on the sofa. Alicia and Simon had arrived perhaps five minutes before in the local taxi, and Alicia had stepped out, superbly groomed, with Simon dancing attendance, staring around so scornfully it was obvious she considered her sister's little country bijou residence a poor substitute for home.

'Well, there's no use hiding, I'd better go down and meet them,' Katie had muttered, leaving Renee with her stomach in knots. This morning her ankle was aching badly, impelling Nick to say she and Katie had better come back to the house so at least he would be there when she needed carrying. Katie had more than half way agreed, when Alicia descended on them.

She came in looking very beautiful and stern, demanding to know what had happened to her daughter.

'Just a little accident, Mother. Nothing!' Renee just brushed her mother's smooth, tinted cheek. 'How are you?'

'Annoyed—and further, upset. Do you think you can get me a couple of tablets, Kate. I have a shocking headache. Such blinding sunlight! Disastrous for the complexion. Renee, I hope you've been wearing a hat.'

Simon came to her and went to kiss her lips, but Renee forestalled him, holding out her hand. 'Hello, Simon, what brings you here? Not a pleasure trip, I'm sure.'

'I've missed you,' he said ardently, and even his eyes were full of feeling. 'You do really love me, darling. Won't you come back with us? It's so infernally hot up here.'

'I like it.'

'You can't mean that!' Alicia stared back at her

oddly. 'What are you thinking about, falling off a horse? You've never done such a thing in the last dozen years.'

'Accidents happen, Mother.' Renee lifted her head as Katie came back into the room. 'But don't worry, it's only a sprain.'

'You look pale.' Simon put out his hand and caressed her hair and Renne had the terrible desire to hit his hand away. How had she ever thought him good-looking? He looked positively foolish, smiling at her, a tailor's dummy with a smooth, clean-cut face.

'Are you staying over?' Katie asked her sister the moment she had disposed of the soluble aspirin.

'Thank you, no.' Even grimacing, Alicia looked stunning. 'We're booked on the return flight and we've secured Renee's ticket.'

'But she's not leaving. . . .'

'She's over what ever it was that was troubling her,' said Alicia, crossing her long slender legs. 'It's time she picked up her life again.'

Renee wanted to shout, but she checked herself. Her mother was always so icily controlled, even in a rage, and she had obeyed her all her life. 'I'm afraid I'm not going, Mother,' she said quietly.

'What did you say?' Alicia pressed her fine-edged lips together, her emerald eyes flashing.

'I'm not going to marry Simon, I'm sorry. I wish you would have listened when I told you on the phone and it would have saved you an unnecessary trip.'

'I think you must be mad!' Alicia rose to her feet, turning the huge emerald ring on her finger. 'You can't go on like this, thrusting off responsibility. You're not in the nursery now, you know, and you can't even give me one good reason why you're up here. You'll be telling me next you want to marry a farmer.'

'What's wrong with that?' Katie swung round. 'At least she wouldn't perish of hunger.'

'Surely you should be making us a cup of tea, Kate?' Alicia smiled coolly at her sister. 'I hope you haven't been filling Renee's head with nonsense?'

'I'll start on the tea,' Katie said quickly, refusing to let Alicia's arrogance reach her. 'Tea for you, Mr Nichols?'

'Simon, please!' Simon wrenched his gaze away from Renee and got to his feet. 'Just what I feel like.'

Katie's face was composed, but there was a blue flame in her eyes. It was a curious thing about power, she noticed. Alicia through her beauty and her husband's wealth had wielded it all her life, but always far more than it was necessary to use. Nick, on the other hand, someone she knew with real power, exercised just enough at a given time so it never became over-used or oppressive. Perhaps that was the secret, to rule with grace.

When Katie returned to the living room, Alicia was still standing over her daughter using the same, hectoring tone. She had spent so long ruling every aspect of her daughter's life, now she couldn't accept Renee's refusal to marry Simon for what it was—her first bid to move out of her mother's reach.

'Do you realise how much you're worrying your father?' Alicia looked down at her daughter's curiously tranquil face.

'Why? Surely there's nothing worrying about staying with my favourite aunt?'

'His concern is, you're neurotic!' Alicia pointed out

with a powerful anger. 'People are asking about you all the time. What are we to tell them? What's Simon to tell them? This holiday with your aunt, won't hold up. It's nearly a month now and time you came back home.'

'To what, Mother?' Renee asked so directly it left Alicia momentarily paralysed.

'To *me*!' Simon sounded shocked. 'Darling, I'll never do anything to worry you again, but please let's make our engagement official.'

'You don't love me,' Renee said.

'I do. Of course I do!' He moved to her eagerly, taking her hands. 'Would I come all this way if I didn't love you?'

'Yes.' Even as she said it, Renee's cheeks flushed scarlet. 'You're a snob and you're very possessive. I just happen to fit your idea of a suitable wife—not perfect, lots of things about me don't appeal to you in the least, but I look the part and my family have got money. Actually I have very little of my own.'

'So you'd better come home!' Alicia knit her delicate brows. 'If you imagine you're going to inherit automatically I must correct you. You've lacked for nothing all your life, now you must do us all credit. You're going to marry Simon as soon as it can be arranged. You never had any doubts before, now you're acting like some timid little rabbit.'

'Correction!' The angry colour sprang to Katie's round cheeks. 'She's acting like her own charming self. You never were a subtle person, Alicia, but I never thought you were cruel. Renee has told you she doesn't love this young man. I don't doubt it comes as a shock. You've never *asked* her anything in her life.'

'Can't we go somewhere together, Renee?' Simon bit his lip. 'I may be able to put things right. I just want you to know I love you and I'll do anything to make you happy.'

'Then go back home, Simon.' Renee lifted her head to look at him. 'It's hard for me to believe you care about me as much as you say, but in any case, I don't care about you.'

'There's another man!' Simon broke in fiercely.

'What, here?' Alicia looked around almost wildly and laughed. 'I don't believe it.'

'It's a fact that Renee has three admirers already,' Katie said, and carried a cup of tea to her sister.

'Oh, Renee, Renee!' Alicia made a helpless little gesture with her hand, 'have you taken leave of your senses?'

'Milk, Simon?' Katie asked politely, and Simon settled back in his chair with the air of a man deeply disturbed.

The talk went on exhaustively for most of the day, and an hour before they were due to take their return flight Nick arrived, immediately aware of the tensions but giving no sign. At least his arrival afforded Katie and Renee some wry amusement, for Alicia, prepared to queen it over some simple country soul, found herself amazed and, more, *managed* so it was Nick who eventually shepherded them into his big, air-conditioned car.

Alicia was smiling, then laughing, and she even held her hand up to wave.

'Good God!' Katie hissed, 'Who would ever have believed it?'

'Mother has never been able to resist a good-looking

man,' Renee pointed out dryly, propped up on the porch where Nick had left her.

'Not so, Simon, he looks furious!' Katie whispered, her face wreathed in hypocritical smiles. 'Goodbye, dear. 'Bye, Simon!'

Alicia pressed the button that lowered her window and smiled brilliantly, a past mistress of the art of cover-up. 'Look after yourself, darling. I'll wait to hear from you.'

'Yes, Mother.' Slowly Renee raised her hand, wanting at this stage no more than to collapse. After such a day, her mother was now looking dazzled and dazzling, utterly beguiled by Nick's charm and that wicked attraction. Add to that the appeal of owning one of the biggest stations in the country and half the town of Garbutt and Nick had the haughty Alicia eating out of his hand. It almost made Renee blush and she turned her head away. Of course her mother had jumped to the conclusion that Nick was one of her 'admirers'. It wasn't true, but it had offered a wonderfully easy solution. Her mother would even forgive her for not marrying Simon if she could win such a fantastic prize as Nick Garbutt.

'Well!' said Katie, bursting out laughing, 'did you ever see such an actress?'

'You're not so bad yourself!' Renee felt so close to weeping it didn't matter, and when Katie turned around she knew it.

'Oh, darling, this has been too much for you!'

'I tried, Katie. I tried, but Mother scarcely listens to a word I say. I don't know what would have happened if Nick hadn't arrived.'

'I suppose he realised that as well,' Katie said thoughtfully. 'He didn't just look in, you know. He was here for a purpose and that was support. Our efforts seemed to be going in vain. I scarcely knew what Alicia planned to do, yell for reinforcements or carry you off herself. She even makes your father jump.'

'Well, she met her match today.'

'Unmistakably!' Katie very nearly crowed. 'And all with such charm. Alicia didn't realise what was happening until she was safely in the car. Honestly, I'll never forget it. Neither will that young man. The moment he kissed you goodbye—for ever!'

When at last Nick returned, he took one look at Renee's exhausted face, then told them both they were coming over to Emerald until Renee was mobile.

'I haven't had time to pack a thing!' Katie gave a sigh of apology. 'Thanks, Nick, for coming to the rescue. It was rather a full day.'

'I can see that!' A little grimly he reached down and scooped Renee out of the planter's chair, carrying her back into the living room and depositing her on the comfortable old sofa. 'I guess I told you to solve your own problems, but not damn well exhaust yourself.'

'Don't bully me, Nick,' she quavered.

'Hell, I'm on your side.' He jerked back a chair and towered over her. 'You look as if you need a couple of pain-killers.'

'I must!' She bent her shining head. 'The others have worn off.'

'They're in the kitchen,' Katie said swiftly.

'I'll get them while you pack.' Nick was already at the kitchen door. 'You don't need much. I expect you'll be wanting to work some part of the time, so I'll get a man to run you back and forth. Martha won't be back until Monday.'

'So I'm the chaperone!' Katie said thoughtfully. 'I fell down on the job last night.'

'Sure it wasn't strategy?' Nick turned to smile at her.

'No, dear, Honey's fault.'

'Which reminds me, you'd better bring her.'

Renee was alone on the rear terrace with Honey fast asleep beside her, when Sharon called. It was next morning and Nick had gone out directly after breakfast, promising to come back to the homestead for lunch.

'Hello there!' Sharon called like a challenge, coming through the sliding glass doors that led to the wonderfully relaxing outdoor entertainment area.

'Hi!' Renee sat up hastily and Honey gave the expected bark and subsided. 'I'm afraid I'm the only one at home. Nick's gone out and Katie's slipped over to the farmhouse for something she forgot.'

'That's all right, it's you I want to see,' Sharon answered with a hard mockery. 'I suppose you think you're very clever?'

'No,' Renee said calmly. 'I'm certain I'm not. Is there something wrong, Sharon?'

'You might well ask!' Sharon's dark eyes showed her hostility. She sank into a wicker chair, facing Renee on the recliner, obviously very het up about something. 'I've heard about your little accident.'

'You don't look very sorry for me.'

'Why should I?' Sharon burst out. 'It was a put-up job, wasn't it?'

'You surely can't believe that?' Renee said expressively. 'It was a very upsetting incident, God knows.'

'Oh yes, but you're not the shy little violet I believed you were. Whew, when you move, you *move*. That is to say, I know you spent the night here and I know Martha wasn't here, much less your aunt. Don't deny it.'

'I wasn't going to,' Renee said mildly. 'Are you concerned about my good name?'

'I'm concerned that you're cheap and easy!' Sharon retorted starkly.

'Thank you, and you take Nick's seduction for granted?'

'So you're beautiful!' Sharon cried passionately. 'Nick's a man!'

'And you're embarrassing. I mean it, Sharon.'

'Are you trying to tell me nothing happened?' Sharon said bitterly.

'I don't have to tell you anything at all!' Anger began to flicker over Renee's calm features. 'If you and Nick are so close why don't you take it up with him?'

'I won't, because he won't like it.' Sharon continued to stare at her with a dark, almost inimical expression. 'You forget what kind of a man Nick is.'

'*I* don't. *You* do!' Renee answered with deliberation, only wishing she could get up and walk away.

Sharon was about to make a furious reply, but she stopped, obviously trying to get a hold on herself. 'Can you blame me?' she asked coldly.

'I know you're not justified in coming up here to ask questions. You're not Nick's wife and you're not his fiancée,' Renee replied.

'I love him!' Sharon's dark eyes were smouldering dangerously. 'Do you think I'm constantly pursuing him for no good reason? Nick's a man of strong passions. Maybe you can confirm that yourself. When he makes love to a woman she becomes too vulnerable to deny him.'

'You would know more about that than I would.' Renee's eyes turned to jade as the shock hit her.

'So you're jealous? I just *knew*!' Sharon dashed up with her dress swirling about her pretty legs. 'So you're in love with him? Why not? I can't hold it against you. Nick's power over women is no secret around here, but he hasn't married a one of them.'

'He's saving himself for you?' Renee lifted her head.

'No,' Sharon answered harshly, 'as far as I'm concerned we were married long ago. All but a bit of paper.'

'Then it's about time he gave you his name.' Renee put her hand to her temple. 'Forgive me, I didn't realise the situation.'

'No.' Sharon's expression lightened. 'You can understand how I feel when I think he's betrayed me.'

'How you're not married is what I can't understand,' Renee said wearily. 'In any case, I've always found Nick a very honourable man.'

'Then you must forgive me!' Sharon pleaded. 'I want us to be friends. You must know Philip has fallen in love with you?'

'How could he?' A spasm passed across Renee's eyes. 'He doesn't even know me nor I him.'

'Yet you let him hold you—*kiss* you.' Sharon's pleading tone became accusing.

'Did he tell you that?' Renee tried to get up, but fell back in pain.

'Of course he did. Pip's never been able to keep any

secrets from me,' Sharon cried. 'Quite obviously you encouraged him and if you didn't mean it, you're a disgrace!'

'I must be,' Renee said wryly. 'First Nick, now Philip. What about Ken Thomas?'

'He prefers me!' Sharon retorted with unexpected pride. 'At one time he even asked me to marry him.'

'In spite of the fact you considered yourself married to Nick?' Renee asked with some sarcasm. 'Tell me, what shameful things have *you* done?'

'How dare you!' For a second Sharon looked demented, then she lurched forward, grasping Renee's hair and pulling it violently. 'Why don't you go away, you're not wanted here!'

'Let *go*!' Sheer shock rendered Renee almost helpless, but Honey sprang up at her target, closing her teeth on Sharon's full skirt, gripping hard and jerking her away.

It looked so funny Renee could have laughed, but the material ripped away and Sharon staggered and fell.

'You brute!' Colour stood up lividly on her tanned cheekbones and she made no attempt to get up.

'Honey—here, girl!' Renee took a deep breath, reaching right over as far as she could go and getting a grip on Honey's tail. 'Quiet, girl. Quiet! Everything's all right!'

'*Is* it?' Sharon shrieked. 'Just look at my dress!'

'Oh, I'm sorry!' Caught between amusement and dismay, Renee watched the other girl get to her feet. 'It was so pretty!'

'Now it's ruined!' Sharon was shouting, tears of rage glistening in her eyes. 'I shall tell Nick everything!'

'About what?'

Nick was moving soundlessly through the door, his dark face hard and assessing. 'Here, Honey!'

The labrador reacted instantly to the voice of authority, ceasing its growling and ambling over to the doorway where it waited in vain for a pat.

'What goes on here?' he asked briefly, moving over to help Sharon to her feet.

'Oh, Nick!' She collapsed against him with a great deal of talent, brushing the back of her hand across her tear-filled eyes. 'Renee set the dog on me.'

'I couldn't. I'm not capable.' Renee met Nick's eyes squarely, knowing something inside her was dying. Surely having led Sharon so far he would marry her?

'She *did*!' Sharon persisted. 'You don't think it would attack me for no reason and just look at my dress!' Still resting against Nick, she lifted the hem of her skirt out showing the jagged hole.

'We'll get you another.' Nick narrowed his eyes at the damage. 'And what did you say that made Renee react in that way?'

'I did nothing,' Renee said wearily, and leaned right back in her reclining chair. She hadn't the least intention of defending herself any further. Sharon could say what she liked.

'It was about Philip,' she heard Sharon's despairing voice say.

'Oh, yes, Philip,' Nick returned crisply. 'What about him?'

'I don't know what Renee intended, but the fact is she's encouraged him to the extent he can't speak of anything else. He's very sensitive, you know, very susceptible. He thinks Renee is the most wonderful thing that ever happened to him, and all because of the other night.'

'And what happened the other night?' Nick asked a little cruelly, 'did she come to his room in his dreams?'

'Don't laugh, Nick!' Sharon implored him.

'Who's laughing?' His silver eyes flashed metallic. 'I can see it now, the green-eyed enchantress playing upon the susceptibilities of this naïve and cloistered boy.'

'It was better than playing!' Sharon shot back tartly. 'She made herself very charming to him, allowing him to make love to her.'

'It wasn't really very pleasant!' Renee said absently, a pounding setting up in her temples.

'Did you let him?' Nick stared back at her, her tilted head showing the lovely line of her chin and throat. 'The poor devil!'

'Of course it's easy for you to laugh,' Sharon challenged him, the flare of passion in her nostrils. 'You've been very wicked in your time, but Pip? Why, he's just a boy!'

'He's a fool!' Nick commented, his eyes so light against his darkly tanned face they were startling. 'He was delirious about Renee from the very first moment he set eyes on her. She helped him by being too kind, but you mustn't blame her for his fantasies. If he really wants someone to care for him I'd suggest he keep dating Thea Grayson. His chances are far better there.'

'So you approve of what she's done?' The tears came to Sharon's eyes again and she jerked away from him as if stung to the bone.

'No, she's got me to reckon with!' Nick threw up his imperious head. 'I'm still waiting to hear the true story.'

'Let's say Renee is jealous of me,' Sharon gave a choked little indrawn breath. 'I like her, but she doesn't like me.'

Nick's eyes, so extraordinarily alive, flicked Renee's prone body. 'Do good-looking women ever care about one another?'

'We could have been friends.' Sharon said pointedly. 'I came over wanting to see how Renee was and was met with nothing but hostility and that vicious dog.'

'Is she? Did she nip you?' Nick's face became faintly derisive. 'Ordinarily she's very friendly. I'm sorry, Sharon. I'll see that dress is replaced. It's so pretty on you, it's a damned shame.'

'That's all right, Nick!' Sharon's face brightened. 'It's not your fault!'

'I suppose it must be mine!' Renee offered impulsively. 'What exactly did I say to make Honey leap upon you?'

'I think I've embarrassed you enough.' Sharon turned back to Nick, a healthy colour in her cheeks. 'In any event, I intend to forget it.'

'That's nice of you, Sharon,' he answered almost gently. 'It might be merciful if you dropped a word of wisdom in Philip's ear. He'll thank you for it later. Forget Renee. I'm afraid she's not for him.'

'From what I've seen, it's just as well!' Sharon said unpleasantly. 'I came over here on a mercy trip, now I'm assaulted.'

'So you've made clear.' Nick glanced at her, saw the tears in her eyes, then abruptly put his arm around her petite figure and drew her to his side. 'Didn't you really come here to do battle?' he asked gently.

'No, Nick!' she whispered, lifting her head to stare into his face.

'It's your nature to speak out, but do let me manage my own affairs.'

'Yes, Nick!' she said almost indistinctly. 'Don't be angry with me. I just thought it necessary to talk to Renee about Philip. I couldn't bear to see him hurt any more.'

'If necessary *I'll* talk to him,' Nick returned dryly. 'Perhaps we've all been a little too soft, a little too kind to Philip. He's inclined to let his emotions run away with him. Surely he knows Renee's already planning to marry someone else?'

'Really?' Sharon's eyes glowed with joy and relief. 'Why didn't you tell me, Renee? I heard about your visitors—it's such a small town.'

Renee was silent, deciding in that instant that silence was golden.

'Can't we be friends?' Sharon's vivacious face cleared miraculously and she slipped out from under Nick's arm, coming over to Renee and holding out her hand.

'Why not? It might be safer,' Renee replied, and suffered the insincere handshake.

Sharon's dark lashes fluttered and she smoothed her torn dress. 'It's such a hot day, I was wondering if I could come over this afternoon and swim?'

'Why not?' Renee sat up and flung her long golden hair over her shoulder. 'As you can see, I won't be able to join you.'

'You forget I'm used to having the run of the house,' Sharon answered with deliberate gaiety. 'Now if you'll both excuse me, I'll run along home. Dad is having a friend over for lunch and I still haven't decided what we're having.'

'I'll see you to the car,' Nick said without hesitation. 'Tell Cy I'll make it into town some time tomorrow morning.'

'Will do!' Sharon stood on tiptoes and kissed him on the cheek. 'It's been a long time since you've been over to dinner.'

'Yes, hasn't it?' He took her arm and turned her towards the door. 'Say goodbye to our little patient.'

'Goodbye, Renee!' Sharon called with no embarrassment at all. 'I'm glad it's no more than a sprain.'

'Me too.' Renee saved herself from bursting out laughing. Either that, or cry. 'I'm really sorry about your dress.'

'Don't mind too much!' Sharon smiled brilliantly, over her shoulder. 'After all, Nick promised me a new one.'

Among other things! Renee lay back and closed her eyes. The days went by. Thursday or the next day she should be able to stand on her feet. Her mind shuddered away from her love scene with Nick. God! She forced herself not to think. How long had Sharon been waiting for Nick to ask her to marry him? If she had known him all her life, it must have been years. Poor Sharon! She was filled with a sense of the most profound disillusionment.

Ten minutes later when Nick came back he found her still with her eyes closed, a melancholy expression of her exquisitely flushed face.

'What's the matter with you?' he asked dryly. 'I leave you for ten minutes and you're somebody else!'

'And who are *you*?' she challenged him, her green eyes sparkling deeply.

'Do I detect censure in those beautiful eyes?' He was looking at her searchingly, but he hadn't lost his mocking smile.

'In any case it's none of my business.' She went to pull herself up, but he dropped down on to the recliner and held her back by the shoulder.

'Lie quietly.'

'Of course I will. I'll do anything I'm told.'

'Are you really jealous?' he asked her with a twist of his mouth.

'Not me. I'm just a passer-by.'

'Not the other night, certainly.'

'You *beast*!' she said, feeling agitated and helpless and trapped.

'Which strikes me it's a pretty good idea to kiss you again. I mean, I'm drawn to you despite myself.' He leaned over, held her head in his hand and kissed her mouth hard.

'That's it, kiss me when I can't fight you,' she whispered, her mouth throbbing and her pulses volcanic.

'Then let's go somewhere where you can!' he flashed back, his silver eyes never leaving her face.

'I choose not to!' Her fingers fluttered away from his hand.

'So? We've proved you're not frigid. What's the outrage in your eyes? Something Sharon has been telling you?'

'She loves you.'

'How nice!' There was anger and mockery in his brilliant eyes. 'And you think I'd better hurry up and marry her?'

'For that matter, I think you should have done it a long time ago,' she said bitterly.

'My God, you women!' He sprang up away from her, radiating a high mettled masculinity. 'I have not, not ever, not once. . . .'

'She told me you *had*!' Renee cut him off recklessly. 'Why are you bothering to lie? I told you it's none of my business!'

'Isn't it?' Standing over her, he looked harsh with contempt. 'You bet it isn't, green eyes!'

'But of course! You can graciously bestow your favours where you please. I want to thank you anyway.' She gave an hysterical little laugh.

'Stop that!' he warned her. 'You're going to control yourself.'

'I want to go inside.' She put her weight on one arm and swung her legs over the side of the recliner wincing a little as the blood rushed to her feet. '*Oh!*'

Immediately Nick was beside her, lifting her into his arms. 'You sounded like a wounded bird.'

'I *am* wounded,' she said mournfully.

'We have an hour before Katie gets back. Shall we make the most of it?' His eyes swept over her face with a mixture of mockery and challenge.

'You're heartless!'

'A callous beast, but it's only you I want.'

'For how long?'

'Who can tell?' His glance slanted unpleasantly over her and warning lights showed in his eyes.

A soft shiver ran through her as he carried her back into the house, so she had to turn her hot face into his throat. 'I wish I'd never met you.'

'No, green eyes, you don't!' His voice was hard and

matter-of-fact and she swallowed convulsively.

'Where are you taking me?'

'You sound nervous,' he drawled.

'You've made me nervous from the first second I laid eyes on you. I knew then you were a hard, uncaring man.'

He reached the library and walked through the open doorway, lowering them both on to the sofa. 'Remember this?'

'I don't want to.' There was a faint violence in him and her eyes went huge.

'Are you going to apologise for casting me as the cad?'

'That's the way it sounded, Nick.'

'Just as you like!' he said insolently, and drew her hair across her throat. His dark head bent over her and she lay bound and captive, her head fallen back against his shoulder.

'I don't want you to kiss me. *Please*, Nick.'

'Oh, I know!' he said jeeringly. 'You want me just as much as I want you. When you're fit enough, I'll prove it.'

'What then?' she taunted him, her satiny skin suffused with colour. 'Do you lose interest?'

'Then I'll have you while it lasts!'

Belatedly she tried to jerk away, but his hand speared through her hair, tightening painfully as he held her head where he wanted it. 'You asked for this.'

'Oh yes, because I'm mad!'

'Fine.' He laughed in his throat. 'I love you mad.'

His hand moved to cup her breast, building the dizzying tension in her, then his mouth closed over her own, not forcing, but generating such excitement, her body was shaken by tremors. She felt frightened, so frightened of his power. She wasn't wearing a bra and now he knew it and was aroused by it, gathering her against him, kissing her mouth and her throat and the satiny skin between her breasts. Little kisses. Terrible kisses—as terrible in daylight as they had been at night. Maybe worse.

'You're beautiful!' His hand moved up to frame her face, the tips of his fingers under her hair. 'Would you let me take you, Sleeping Princess?'

'Not in broad daylight!' Her answer shocked her even more than his low laugh.

'Actually it's delicious. You make me ache inside. It's strange!' He turned her head gently to kiss under her ear and the base of her throat. 'No woman has ever succeeded in doing that.'

'So that puts me on top of the list. How many after?' she asked shakily.

'Dozens, I'm afraid, in my younger days. Do you want me to stop?'

His voice sounded lazy, but there was an urgency in him that corresponded to her own: an unappeased exacerbation, muscles tensing, aroused breathing. She twisting nearer as his hand stroked her skin, his mouth hungry as he pulled her to him, effectively shattering her, the initiative all his, kissing her in a way she was unlikely to forget. Loving her, or insulting her flagrantly, she couldn't measure which.

'Why aren't you telling me you love me?' He bit gently on her ear. So gently, his hand circling her breast.

'What *is* love?' The cry was wrenched from her in a half blind frustration because the way he felt about her wasn't the same. 'What is it, please tell me?'

'No, Renee,' he lifted his head to look down at her, 'I'll leave you to find out yourself.'

CHAPTER SEVEN

It was three months before the Caswell exhibition opened in Sydney. Three months of change. Renee had found herself a job as assistant to the production manager of a leading beauty and fashion magazine and with a good weekly salary she had found herself a pleasant flat that would fit neatly into her parents' palatial Roman bathroom with room for a grand piano.

Still, it was hers, and new friends were always coming by. Not the socialites she had been surrounded by all her life, but the people she worked with and the advertising crowd. At first she was sure it was her background that had gained her the job; an appearance enhanced by all the expensive clothes from her former life, but when she overheard Lucy Kaplan describe her as 'my right hand' her self-doubts disappeared.

Work was her salvation. Lucy kept her at it until she was ready to drop. But at least she didn't have time to stop and think. Except now and again when she cried herself to sleep.

Nick.

On the nights when the flat seemed unbearably silent, she would shift all the furniture about, or wash her hair, or feverishly jot down new ideas for Lucy. Lucy seemed to enjoy them and said she had flair, even with the decorating of the flat. Her mother had refused to come anywhere near the place, extra scathing, but her father had come, looking around with a kind of incredulous anguish. Then he had put an arm across her shoulders and marched her out to dinner, making the interesting remark that he had warned her mother this would happen.

She didn't see Simon at all, which was perfect. Simon belonged to her past—a shadow figure, someone vague and faceless. Being a blonde and good-looking, she had any number of admirers and refusing them kept her very, very busy. She had been so sadly deceived in the past. One day she would accept someone, when she had put it all behind her.

Nick. Emerald. Except that she couldn't.

Of course she kept in touch with Katie—letters, phone calls. She loved to hear Katie's voice, but whenever she mentioned Nick, which was often, pain like an iron band clamped around Renee's heart. Those were the nights she cried herself to sleep only to have Nick come to life in her dreams. Nick, his lordly looks and his monstrous arrogance. Just to fall in love with him had been shameful but oh, so memorable. She couldn't erase him from her mind.

Now Harry, with his work finished, was in Sydney for the first night of the showing. Renee had watched him on television the night before, feeling very proud and tearful. He had looked every inch the creative artist, larger than life size, and he had paid public tribute to Katie's unstinting encouragement. Katherine Anne Ingram, that is, a highly regarded artist in her own right.

Renee had sat there in front of her small rented T.V. set, letting her coffee go cold while the silly weak tears sprang to her eyes. Harry brought it all back— Emerald, the tropics, explosive emotion. The only time in her life she had really lived. Now it was over.

She went to bed grief-filled but still managed to pick
out a new dress for the showing. Katie was flying in
about an hour before the six o'clock preview and they
had arranged that she would come back to the flat to
stay on for a few days. Of course there was only one
bedroom, but Renee didn't in the least mind sleeping
on the sofa. There was no comfort anywhere and she
had lost so much weight she was almost insubstantial.

There was no time to go home after work, but when
she freshened up in the washroom and changed into
her dress she knew she looked beautiful. Lucy and a
few of her colleagues had waited behind to check over
her appearance and their comments should have lifted
her morale to the skies, only her green eyes were desperate. Katie had told her Nick had insisted on flying
them all in and from bitter experience she knew his
effect on her. Except now she was a working girl in a
big city and nothing was wrong with her brain or her
ability to mix with people. Being with Lucy had proved
that. She looked as cool as a lily with her long gleaming
hair arranged in a smooth coil, her pared down and
polished white silk suit belted around her narrow
waist. Lucy called it clean-cut dressing, but one had to
be tall and slim to wear it with the extra bonus of a
small waist. If she could act as cool as she looked, it
would be indeed remarkable.

When Harry spotted her across the crowded room,
he immediately broke away from the admiring group
around him and came towards her, taking her into his
strong arms.

'Renee, is it possible you've become more beautiful?'

'How lovely to see you, Harry!' She drew back to

smile at him. 'Although I saw you on the T.V. last night. You were very commanding.'

'I made myself think positive before I went on. Katie hasn't arrived yet. Nor Nick. I suppose you know he was flying in?'

'Yes.' Renee saw the kindness and understanding in his eyes. 'Don't worry, this is going to be a wonderful night. Everything looks terrific and it's so perfectly displayed.

'Goldman knows his job.' Harry glanced around at the big display of pottery and sculpture. 'I hope you're ready to pose beside your head. It's already caused a considerable flutter, in fact there are a number of eyes on you now.'

'Then you can't guarantee me anonymity?' She glanced into his piercing blue eyes, willing the butterflies in her tummy to go away.

'Sorry, dear, we're making one another famous. There are four stickers on it already with a limited edition of six. I'm even embarrassed to tell you the price, but of course Goldman has to make something as well.'

Time passed. Renee went with Harry, drawn into conversation with different groups. Everyone appeared to be having a wonderful time and the champagne flowed freely. Renee was suddenly aware of some applause on her left, of Harry's leonine head turning in that direction, then as she moved slightly herself, she saw Katie in the doorway, making a warm, enveloping gesture with both hands, more applause from the large sprinkling of fellow artists, then Sharon and Ken Thomas and—*Nick.*

'Harry!' Katie cried, and Harry swung through the room to meet her with a marked show of eagerness.

It wasn't easy to follow, but Renee's pride made her go. If it killed her she was going to play the part of a young woman with not one care in the world. Katie hugged her and held her close for a long moment and told her she looked wonderful, and somehow she found the strength to look at Nick.

'How are you, Nick?' She held out her hand as expected, already gone. Lost.

He didn't hesitate but bent his dark head to kiss her cheek. 'What have you been doing to yourself, Renee? You look breakable.'

'Actually I've never felt better!' It sounded very cool and sweet and her green gaze moved on to Sharon and Ken. 'How lovely to see you!'

Ken greeted her with a kiss and a cry of delight, but Sharon's dark eyes had a peculiar glitter in their depths.

'You *have* lost weight, Renee,' she murmured, brows raised.

'Perhaps a little, I'll admit!' Renee gave a little laugh. 'It's hard for me to believe three months have slipped past.'

'Three months, one week and four days,' Nick said unexpectedly. 'I've done my bit of counting, you see.'

It wasn't the time to stand about talking, for it was Harry's job to circulate and if possible pontificate on his own work, and Nick was directing swift, interested looks about the large room; the pieces of sculpture beautifully lit and displayed on tall columns, the magnificent ceramic forms and the pots and platters and blossom jars set out on long low tables or on the floor.

'A remarkable collection, Harry.'

'Yes, it's going rather well!' Harry looked boyishly pleased. 'There are some people I want you to meet, Nick ... Katie,' he turned to her, taking her arm with a curious look of permanence. 'You girls coming?'

From the archway leading to another room someone called: 'Ken Thomas!' and Ken, wearing a very stylish suit and a striped shirt, turned his tawny head and called back:

'Sawbones—good God!'

For a moment he stood transfixed, just staring, then he turned back to Renee and Sharon, who as yet hadn't followed the others. 'Excuse me, girls. I won't be a moment. I'm not going to allow you to meet this bloke until I'm sure he's absolutely sober.'

'Plenty of time!' Sharon said lightly, and waved him away.

Now they were alone, Renee saw further evidence of hostility in Sharon's tight smile. She was looking very glamorous in her favourite neon-bright scarlet and as she lifted a hand to brush away a non-existent wisp of hair from her temple, Renee caught the glitter of a beautiful solitaire diamond.

'Surprised?' Sharon asked with some malice.

Floored, Renee thought, momentarily struck speechless. How was she going to get through this night?

'Then you do still love him?' Sharon said musingly. 'I thought so.'

'On the contrary, I'd like to offer my best wishes,' Renee said gallantly, made stronger by Sharon's obvious cruelty. 'Tell me, when is the wedding to be?'

'Almost immediately.' Sharon glanced down again at her pretty hand. 'We're to have our honeymoon in

Hawaii, then on to the West Coast of the States. Don't look so heartbroken!' There was a grim smile on her small scarlet mouth.

'Pardon me, but I'm not.' Renee was astonished at how cool and calm she sounded, but she was very pale. 'You'll excuse me, won't you, Sharon. I assume you're trying to upset me, so there's no point in staying together.'

'Poor little Renee!' Sharon drawled in a relentless undertone. 'Who was it who really drove you out of paradise? It wasn't *me*!'

Distressed, Renee stared at her, then turned away. It was a bitter pleasure to know Sharon still counted her as a rival even with Nick's ring on her finger. He mightn't know it, but he would have a lifetime of an almost frighteningly jealous wife.

'My dear Renee!'

Someone approached Renee and grasped her arm and as she looked around she saw it was a friend of her father's, an avid collector of sculpture.

'Mr Harrington, how nice to see you!'

'I've just arrived,' he told her. 'Helen's looking at that perfectly splendid head. It's yours, of course?'

'Yes, I was the model.' Renee smiled into his shrewd but kindly eyes.

'Look here, my girl, I've simply got to have one, yet there are stickers all over the darned thing. Where's your father?' Clive Harrington bore her off to where his wife was standing, apparently captivated, and at least she received a warm reception there. Helen Harrington was a nice woman, warm and sincere, and just being with her allowed Renee to recover to the extent she felt she could get through another hour. If her scars were showing on the outside, people would turn away from her in horror.

Katie came up and spoke for a moment, clasping her hands together almost ecstatically. 'It's going wonderfully well. Even Roger loves everything!' She named one of the country's most distinguished and influential critics.

'Katie,' Clive Harrington grabbed her arm, 'you've got to do your best to get me one of these heads. Absolutely superb! Knew it was Renee right away.'

'But there are only six, dear!'

'In that case, I shall commission another.'

Smilingly Renee excused herself. It could have been such an enjoyable and harmonious evening, but inside she was shaking with shock. Why shock? she demanded of herself. Hadn't she known this was going to happen? Ken was still talking cheerfully to the tall, bespectacled man he had called Sawbones, but she couldn't see Sharon or Nick. They had to be in the other room, which meant she had to stay here. If only the pounding in her head would quieten! She had never felt more miserable in her life, but she couldn't permit herself to show it.

'Nick, I've lost you ... *lost you*. You never had him, another voice inside her head said.

Someone took her arm with a surprisingly strong and swift motion and as she glanced up in amazement Nick said incredibly: 'Well, I've been through all the motions, I've spent a few thousand dollars, now I'm only going to look at what belongs to me.'

'How do I come into it?' she asked caustically, still wanting him and needing him so much, and it was all over and she couldn't understand.

'Come with me and I'll tell you. *Now!*' There was a look on his handsome face that told her not to fight him. Not here where it was so dreadfully public.

'For God's sake, Nick!' Somehow he had forced her outside and they were walking towards one of the cars parked in the private courtyard. 'Do you enjoy doing this kind of thing? Do you think it's fun!'

'Cut it out!' he returned almost roughly. 'It's been a long day.'

'Don't you know you've got a fiancée inside?'

'What the hell? ... you little fool!' he snapped, and almost pushed her into the car.

'I don't believe this!' Renee was crying suddenly, but he ignored her, reversing out of the driveway and on to the narrow, car-lined street.

'Where's this apartment of yours?' he asked, in a hard fed-up voice that sent vibrations right through her.

'You don't think....'

'I said *where*?' He didn't shout, but he didn't have to.

'Not far. First turn on the right, then go up to the lights.'

She scarcely knew what to expect, startled out of her tears.

'Now what?' His silver eyes narrowed over her as they sat at the red light. 'Just give me directions, that's all.'

Oddly intimidated, she did so and after fifteen minutes of weaving through heavy traffic they arrived at her door.

'Open up,' Nick ordered briefly.

'I can't find the key.'

'Of course not!' He took her bag, rummaged through

it, and came up with the key, inserting it in the door. 'After you.'

She looked at him quickly, trying to gauge his strange mood, but there was scarcely enough light.

'So this is where you live,' said Nick.

'It's the best I can do on my salary.' Her legs were trembling so much she had to sit down. She had long ago stopped wondering what was going on. Nick would tell her in his own good time.

'Ah yes, Katie told me about your job. So now you've proved you're a smart girl.' He paused, picked up an ornament and put it down. 'Must I look at you from over there?'

'This isn't kind, Nick,' she said brokenly, and made a helpless little movement of her hand. 'What *is* it you want of me?'

'The truth!' He turned his head and Renee saw his eyes. They flashed across her with a startling brilliance and she felt herself succumbing, somewhat frightened, and powerless to move. Nothing had changed. It would always be this way with Nick. She put her head down and began to weep.

Of course he was there and she wanted him, but she had learned one couldn't live without self-respect.

'*Don't*, Nick!' She loved him so deeply, he would have to help her.

'Don't what? Don't kiss you? God, I can't leave you alone!'

Cradled in his arms, she still looked up at him unflinchingly. 'I can't get into this cheap and terrible situation.'

'All right, tell me all about it,' he invited, holding her away from him with hard, hurting hands.

'Haven't you thought once of fidelity?'

'I put it out of my mind the moment I met you.' His mouth curved in a mocking smile and he put up his hand and released the golden coil of hair at her nape. 'The question is have you been faithful to me in this short exile?'

'Please, please, *please*, Nick, aren't you thinking of Sharon?' Renee was moaning in desperation, a sound that was cut off as his mouth took hers violently and his arms locked around her so tightly she had to cling to him to survive. And then there was nothing in the world but Nick, his warmth and strength, the incredible dizzying desire, that made her senseless, mindless, a willing captive at last.

'I love you, Renee,' he said simply.

'No, Nick.'

'I love you!'

His voice was so tender, so possessive, it belonged in her dreams.

'I love you too!' she said, then all the joy seemed to go out of her. 'I want to hear about Sharon.'

His eyes coveted her beautiful, slender body, and she wondered if there was something radically wrong with her. He *couldn't* kiss her like this—tortuously arouse her and then go back to Sharon.

'Haven't you heard?' he was saying drily. 'She got herself engaged to Ken.'

'*What?*' Her green eyes looked shocked and he kissed them gently.

'No more than a week ago. So that's what it's all about? She told you she was wearing my ring?'

'No, no,' Renee looked at his face again. 'I just stupidly believed it.'

'You forget, darling, I know Sharon.'

'Yet she's marrying Ken?'

'I suppose so,' he said without interest. 'Whatever Sharon told you, and I have to be a part of it, it simply isn't true. Oh, I know how she imagined she felt about me, but only because she lived in a small world. I've never loved a woman in my life before you. In fact I fell in love with you the same day I brought you back to Katie. It all happened so suddenly, and you're so young!'

'So you let me die for three months?'

'You're damned right!' He covered her mouth again, kissing her with increasing passion. 'Tell me, baby, have you suffered enough?' His silver eyes blazed at her, devouring her face. 'It's been hell not having you close to me, but you were always there when I was alone. At the homestead. In the lonely wilderness. I want you for ever.'

'And you thought I didn't know my own mind?' Her face reflected her feelings as clearly as a mirror. 'But it's incredible!'

'You have to be sure, darling, because I'll never let you go. Not until the day I die, and then I mightn't let you go.' He pulled her closer into his arms with the urgent pressure of wanting her and saw tears in her wonderful eyes.

'If that's a life sentence, I thank God.'

'Renee.' For the first time she saw the naked longing in his face, the love she couldn't do without.

'I've been so unhappy!' she whispered.

'You have me now,' he kissed her softly, 'at least until Katie and Harry arrive. They're coming back to the apartment.'

'So Katie knows?' she could see herself reflected in those sparkling grey eyes.

'Darling, Katie's always known,' he murmured, and urgently stopped all her questions.

4 FREE

Harlequin Romances

TAKE THESE 4 FREE

Harlequin Romances

Thrill to romantic, aristocratic Istanbul, and the tender love story of a girl who built a barrier around her emotions in ANNE HAMPSON's "Beyond the Sweet Waters" . . . a Caribbean island is the scene setting for love and conflict in ANNE MATHER's "The Arrogant Duke" . . . exciting, sun-drenched California is the locale for romance and deception in VIOLET WINSPEAR's "Cap Flamingo" . . . and an island near the coast of East Africa spells drama and romance for the heroine in NERINA HILLIARD's "Teachers Must Learn."

Harlequin Romances . . . 6 exciting novels published each month! Each month you will get to know interesting, appealing, true-to-life people . . . . You'll be swept to distant lands you've dreamed of visiting . . . . Intrigue, adventure, romance, and the destiny of many lives will thrill you through each Harlequin Romance novel.

Get all the latest books before they're sold out!

As a Harlequin subscriber you actually receive your personal copies of the latest Romances immediately after they come off the press, so you're sure of getting all 6 each month.

Cancel your subscription whenever you wish!

You don't have to buy any minimum number of books. Whenever you decide to stop your subscription just let us know and we'll cancel all further shipments.